YOUR PERS

EAT SMART
MOVE MORE
SLEEP RIGHT

Take care of your body. It's the only place you have to live.
~ Jim Rohn

LUKE COUTINHO

ISBN 978-93-81115-85-5

Cover Mishta Roy
Layouts Ajay Shah

Published in India 2011 by
BODY & SOUL BOOKS
An imprint of
LEADSTART PUBLISHING PVT LTD
Trade Centre, Level 1
Bandra Kurla Complex, Bandra (E), Mumbai 400 051, INDIA
T + 91 22 40700804 **F** +91 22 40700800
E info@leadstartcorp.com **W** www.leadstartcorp.com

US Office
Axis Corp
7845 E Oakbrook Circle
Madison, WI 53717, USA

Disclaimer
This journal can be used with virtually any fitness program and food plan but it does not make suggestions about how much or what kind of exercise or food you need. That is the role of your trainer and nutritionist. We recommend you discuss your plan with a doctor before starting.

To my family ~
Dad, Mom, Luanne, Aldrin, Declan,
Reuben, Byron, Clive, Roxanne,
Bronco, Thunder, Sneaky & Diesel (RIP)
~ my constant reminders that life is
beautiful. Thank you for your
unconditional love.

This book is for each of you.

About The Author

Luke Coutinho believes in natural health and fitness, and in achieving the same through simple, uncomplicated methods. His clients range from CEO's, MD's, company presidents, celebrities, entrepreneur's and businessmen to priests, nuns, social workers, the less fortunate and the people who need guidance and motivation to get fit and stay motivated. This diverse mix of clientele is spread globally across New York, Canada, Europe, Far East and India. He has been successful in coaching people on general fitness, wellness and lifestyle, and in the fields of weight-loss, adult and child obesity.

Luke is tied up with several NGO's and educates children and parents on basics of nutrition to help combat rising malnutrition numbers. His passion towards educating people about cancer and other diseases has got him currently involved with renowned hospitals in the U.S, for research and procurement of natural foods and papaya brews to prevent and aid in the cure of cancer. Luke has been working with IBM GPS for over 8 years and his work experience includes India, Dubai, Qatar, Belgium, New York and the UK.

Luke can be reached at: luke.coutinho@gmail.com

What do you gain from a balanced and natural food and exercise plan?

Healthy weight.

Reduced risk of life threatening diseases.

More energy.

Age gracefully.

Look and feel good.

Good internal body health.

Superior mental capability.

Great health and fitness levels.

Stress free mind.

Fat loss.

Strong body.

Increased metabolism.

Strong bones.

Elevated self-esteem.

Contents

Part One

- ✓ Introduction.
- ✓ Nutritionist's notes.
- ✓ Tips for using your journal (with examples).
- ✓ EFS Model of Fitness.

Part Two

- ✓ Recording stats.
- ✓ Weekly goals.
- ✓ Daily activity pages.
- ✓ Scribble space.

Part Three

- ✓ Weekly progress charts.
- ✓ Congratulations.
- ✓ In Gratitude.

INTRODUCTION

I strongly believe that man complicates things, way too much.

We have more gyms, health clubs and health foods available and we have more disease and obesity.

We have more elaborate security systems and we have more crime.

We have strong and multiple education systems and we have more children taking to drugs and other illegal activities.

We have more money and less time.

This book is not based on the lifestyles or regimes of celebrities or the rich and the famous. The intention is to reach out to common people and inspire them to believe that they can get fit and healthy today, in the simplest way possible.

We must understand that our bodies are built differently. What works for someone else, may not work for you. Fitness is a result of so many factors: Your lifestyle, genes, the food you eat, the kind of exercise you choose, the amount of sleep you get, and most importantly, your mental attitude and the kind of goals you shape for yourself.

This compilation is based on simple and basic principles and facts that have always existed, but have gotten twisted, complicated by man and have become expensive over time.

You don't need to spend extravagantly to get fit; neither do you need fancy gym memberships. I want everyone to understand the basics of getting fit and healthy, and to start doing so. If you are told to eat or not to eat a certain food, do a certain exercise for a particular duration, ask why. When you understand the logic and gain this knowledge, you automatically begin to incorporate change because you understand it. No one can tell you what to do, and make you do it, unless you accept it and make a personal decision to do it. That comes from within you. It comes from understanding why, and accepting the change.

Success will follow when you know what you want, and you work towards it.

Time and again it has been proven that writing things down can help you become more organized, focused and committed to your goals. When you see your efforts in black and white, you will be better able to analyze progress and detect areas that need improvement.

This is your support tool - 60 days success journal, which will support and guide you over the next 60 days until you have firmly established new habits of eating, exercise and sleep ,to make your body last you a lifetime.

As time passes, your journal will continue to help you stay motivated and on track. Your journey to a healthier body and lifestyle begins with your first entry, and as days go by and blank pages get inked or penciled in, you create a personal memoir of important achievements, a fitter you.

"Keeping a journal will absolutely change your life

in ways you have never imagined"

- OPRAH WINFREY

NUTRITIONIST NOTES

Fitness is the new global buzzword. Wikipedia best defines 'Fitness' as "A general state of good health, usually as a result of exercise and nutrition."

To attain desired levels of fitness, you must have three crucial elements as part of your lifestyle.

These three elements work hand in hand. You cannot achieve fitness levels with just one or two of these three elements. I like to refer to it as the "EFS" model – Exercise, food and sleep.

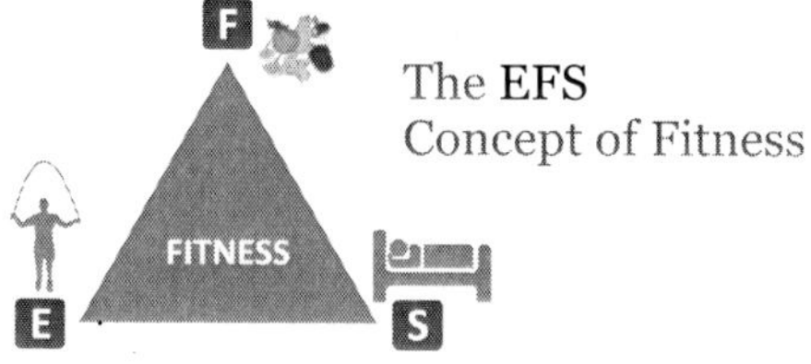

You may have the best food plan and sufficient exercise, but without sufficient sleep, your body will not have time to recover or carry out important hormonal functions related to weight loss, hair, skin and other important functions.

You may have the best food plan and sleep, but without exercise your bones will get weaker, your cardiovascular and lung health will deteriorate and your fat percentage may increase. You will feel tired and lethargic even though you may have slept sufficiently.

Without a balanced food plan, you will maintain an unhealthy weight; the health of your hair, skin and internal body organs will deteriorate.

That is why all of these three elements are required for attaining fitness levels and great health.

"We are what we eat. Food can cure diseases, prevent them, alleviate conditions, help us age gracefully. We need to treat food and the way we eat it with respect and awareness."

Using natural foods, making small lifestyle changes and treating your body with respect is all it takes to live a healthy and happy life.

In today's changing world and environment, it is important that the human race understands that a lifestyle change is equally important.

This lifestyle change that I'm talking about is the inclusion of the three elements viz. exercise, sleep and nutrition. It's really that simple.

Humans tend to complicate everything in life. We have high tech gyms, diet plans based on food science, luxury weight loss camps and spas, and tons of weight loss equipment products. It's all good. Getting fit and staying that way is really simple. You have got to keep it simple. By incorporating the three elements mentioned above into your lifestyle, you will get to your fitness goals.

I encourage everyone to know his or her 'goals'. Is it weight loss, more muscle, general health, sport training or any other. Once you know your goal, planning the milestones to reach there will be simple.

Your goal should be 'Fitness'. Weight loss, muscle, tone, stamina, agility, flexibility, balance, cardiovascular health and mental stability are all a part of fitness. They become your milestones.

For example, if you achieve weight loss, you may be at your desired weight, but what is the health of your lungs, your heart, and your energy levels?

You may have a six-pack, but maybe at the cost of your hair or with haggard looks due to improper rest, over training and insufficient nutrition.

Make 'Fitness' your goal, and you will automatically and easily achieve the milestones during the journey.

Again all these 'milestones' will be achieved by making a balanced choice of exercise, nutrition and sleep, the EFS model.

Exercise:

→ Choose an exercise that you enjoy doing. You may have a variety of exercises that you may like. Use the journal to help plan them all into your weekly schedule.

→ Be careful of injury. It is always safety first. You want exercise to work for you and not against you.

→ Be aware of the changes that exercise brings to your body and mind.

→ If you miss out a few days, it's okay, just get back on track the next day. Everyone has missed days, and sometimes weeks of exercise due to various reasons. Just start again.

→ Understand the importance of exercise, what it does for your body and health and keep it simple. Complication is bad.

Sleep:

- ➔ You need 7 hours of sleep to be your target on a daily basis.
- ➔ When you sleep your body carries out several important functions. Less sleep interrupts these functions.
- ➔ Making up for lost sleep over the weekends is not a solution.
- ➔ People who sleep less tend to have more issues with weight, stress and disease.

Food and Nutrition:

- ➔ Choose foods from the food pyramid (shared in the next chapter)
- ➔ Eat a balanced diet, and if you are modifying it to achieve some fitness goal, do it under professional guidance.
- ➔ Food cures and prevents disease. Educate yourself on the nutritional power of different foods.
- ➔ Eat small meals every two and half to three hours.
- ➔ Never miss a meal or starve yourself. You will become FAT.
- ➔ Drink loads of water through the day.
- ➔ Yes it's true; eat breakfast like a king, lunch like a prince and dinner like a pauper.

I will now share with you two golden eating rules. If you master these, you will never have to be on a diet again. I repeat, Never.

EAT SLOW: Take a morsel, put your spoon and fork down, chew the morsel of food slowly, real slow, connect with your food, try and understand the spice in it, the different flavors, chew it well and then swallow.

What happens when you eat slowly?

- ➔ Digestion starts in your mouth. By the time your well-chewed food reaches your stomach, it's partly digested, enabling the complete digestion to happen quickly in your stomach and eliminating chances for any food to be stored away as fat.

- ➔ When you eat slowly, you will find that you eat much less than you would usually eat if you ate fast. It is true that the stomach takes about 20 minutes to send a signal to your brain saying that you are full. Try serving yourself with half your usual portion and eat slowly. You will find that you will fill up sooner.

- ➔ All problems of gas, acidity, heartburn, indigestion will disappear for good.

→ Most of us tend to eat more than our bodies require, because we eat too fast. When you eat slowly, you will consume the right amount of food that your body requires, and this will do away with consuming extra calories that make you fat.

STOP WHEN FULL: For this to happen you will have to listen to your body. Pay attention and focus. When you feel full STOP EATING. Push your plate away. I know you may waste food by doing this, but in a few days you will automatically serve yourself less food and there will be no wastage.

Follow these two golden rules and you will never have to diet again. You can enjoy all of your favorite foods. Pizza and ice cream too. But eat slowly and stop when you're full, even if you have half a slice of pizza left or half a scoop of ice-cream. Just stop.

Practice these two rules diligently and savor the results you reap.

The 'food and exercise journal' is designed to help you track important records as you adopt the EFS model.

Food and exercise journals are a powerful tool if you want to learn the art of intuitive eating.

What is intuitive eating?

Intuitive eating is listening to your body to choose your foods instead of relying on external regimes and rules. In today's diet obsessed society, most people have moved far from the concept of intuitive eating because they try to intellectualize their diets by attempting to adhere to rigid calorie limits or by deeming particular food groups off-limits. By creating such restraints, the general reaction is to rebel against them and you automatically begin to crave more calories and the very foods which you are 'not supposed' to be eating. Intuitive eating with a food journal can counter this unhealthy and derailing behavior because you allow yourself to eat ANYTHING. However, because you are keeping a food journal, you will be a lot more likely to listen to your hunger/energy needs when making your food choices because you will have to reveal everything you consume in the food journal.

Food and exercise journaling is about listing everything that you eat, not just meals. Any time that you snack, you will want to list it in your food journal. By being honest with yourself and your food journal, you will see the greatest weight loss results and fitness levels.

As you write about what you are eating, think about what you were feeling when you ate. Were you hungry or were you bored? By noting your emotions and feelings in your food and exercise journal, you will begin to see patterns in how you eat. To lose weight, you only want to eat when you are hungry. By identifying other emotions that cause you to eat, you will be able to eliminate them from your diet and life.

Food and exercise journaling is a tool that will help you to evaluate and track your diet. This is a key factor in being successful when it comes to any diet plan. You need to be able to hold yourself accountable for what you eat and to see your progress as you go through your weight loss plan.

Benefits of journaling food,exercise and sleep:

➔ Track down those "extra" calories that sneak into your diet: you might be surprised at how many calories you consume at the end of the day. Even if you ate "healthy" for breakfast, lunch and dinner, all those little snacks you thought were harmless can really add up.

➔ Know when you can cheat: If your are below your caloric goal for the day and you haven't cheated in a few days, then you know you can afford to have a bowl of ice cream or whatever you're craving at the moment.

➔ Increase your self-control: Consciously knowing that you have to write down everything you eat may help you pass on that dessert or second helping.

➔ Overcome plateaus: Everybody hits plateaus while on their diets and there is no easier way to blast through this than by going through your food journal and seeing where you can easily make changes to start losing weight again.

➔ Record your exercise: Record the types of exercise you do along with the time invested. View weekly reports to see how your efforts pay off in terms of weight loss, body build and general fitness. It really works and you will just look and feel so good.

➔ Keep track of your sleep: Daily records of your previous night's sleep will help keep you on track and help understand why you may be feeling so tired and fatigued by the weekend. It will motivate you to get your sleep time back in line.

➔ Record your emotions: Most of us eat out of emotion. We may not be hungry, but we still eat. Recording these moments helps us identify these triggers to emotional eating and slowly and steadily we learn to overcome them, and eat only when our body needs food.

➔ Motivation: It can be very motivating to look through your food and exercise journal and see how far you've come, the success you've had and to be able to visualize how far you can go in the future.

Most people, who have had success with the use of this tool, suggest writing in it as accurately as possible, as often during the day so you don't miss out on anything, and just before sleeping, complete the page and review it.

It does not take more than 5 minutes and most users swear that it makes them feel good, they look forward to ending their day by writing in this diary and reflecting on their performance. Some get creative and start recording other personal comments and emotions too.

Your journey to fitness begins now. Shape your goal and shape up. When you have your goal shaped, you program your mind to want to achieve something. You give your mind a purpose to work towards. You then have an aim and objective, and with an aim and objective comes the direction.

I wish you good luck, great health, happiness, love and peace.

**"In modern life today you either live your dream or off someone else's.
Unless you give your dreams the time and space to express itself,
you will spend the better part of your life living the dreams of other people"
- Stephan Clandler**

TIPS FOR USING YOUR JOURNAL

The food and exercise journal has room for eight weeks (56 days) of journaling. However, since the pages are not predated, it can be used daily or intermittently, and may last longer.

The journal is partitioned in the following sections:

1) **Sharing Stats and Goals – On this page, you can list your current stats, measurements and other facts. Next to that you can list the goals you would strive to reach over the next 8 weeks.**

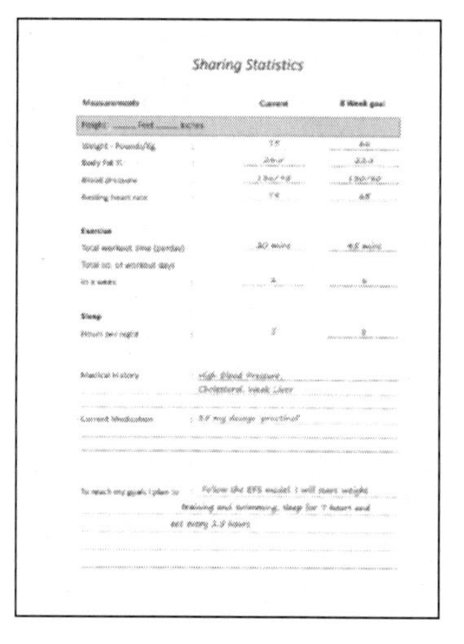
Sharing Statistics

2) **Weekly Plan and Goals – Now that you have your thirteen-week goals planned, a written plan of action is a good idea. This will enable you to break your larger goals into smaller milestones, which become easy to track.**

Weekly Goals

3) **Daily Activities page –**
This is the real thing. Each 'day' consists of two pages. The left hand page focuses on 'food and nutrition' entries. It also records the hours of sleep you got the previous night.

The right hand page allows you to record details of your exercise and fitness program. In addition you can record several other things, like about your trainer, your work out buddy, mood, emotions and comments on how your day went, injuries if any and tips. You also get to rate your performance.

Date: 1-3-11 | Week: # 1 | Day: # 1 | Day of week: Tuesday
No. of hours sleep 7

Food Notes

Upon wake up
warm water, apple

Breakfast
oats, pear, slim milk

Snack 1
6 almonds, green tea

Lunch
whole wheat veg s/w, 1 cup butter milk

Snack 2
2 dried apricots, 1 banana,
1 fatty milk bar

Snack 3
protein shake 5 raisins

Dinner
Carrot soup, tossed salad, mushroom stir fry

Before Sleep
1 teaspoon sunflower seeds

Food tip
Eat Slow
Stop When Full

Did you eat any "comfort food"?
Y ☑ N ☐

Chocolate bar

Bored

Water ☑ ☑ ☑ ☑ ☑ ☑ ☑ ☑ ☑
☑ ☑ ☑ ☐ ☐ ☐ ☐ ☐ ☐

Vitamins / Supplements Y ☑ N ☐
Eat slow ? Y ☑ N ☐
Stop when full ? Y ☑ N ☐

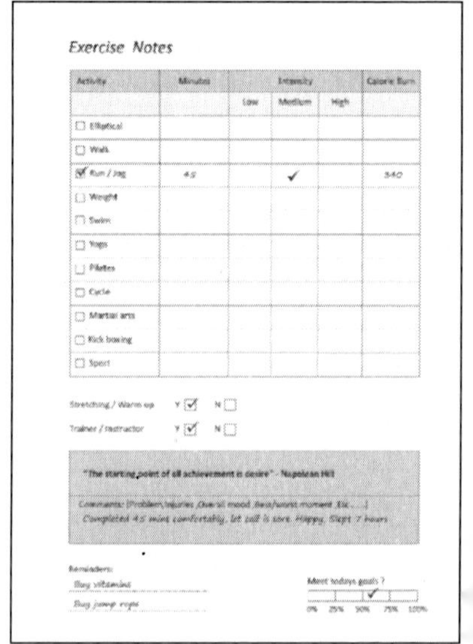

Exercise Notes

Activity	Minutes	Intensity			Calorie Burn
		Low	Medium	High	
☐ Elliptical					
☐ Walk					
☑ Run / Jog	45		✓		340
☐ Weight					
☐ Swim					
☐ Yoga					
☐ Pilates					
☐ Cycle					
☐ Martial arts					
☐ Kick boxing					
☐ Sport					

Stretching / Warm up Y ☑ N ☐
Trainer / Instructor Y ☑ N ☐

"The starting point of all achievement is desire" - Napoleon Hill

Completed 45 mins comfortably, lot call is sore. Happy. Slept 7 hours

Reminders:
Buy vitamins
Buy jump rope

Meet todays goals ?
0% 25% 50% 75% 100%

4) Scribble Space –

At the end of each week you have a page to fill up – questions that help you reflect on the week gone by, emotions and feelings to keep you motivated and ready to dive into the next week.

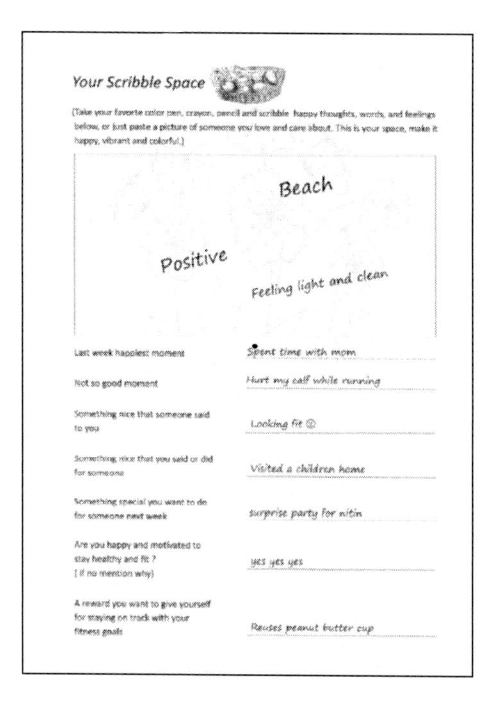

Your Scribble Space

(Take your favorite color pen, crayon, pencil and scribble happy thoughts, words, and feelings below, or just paste a picture of someone you love and care about. This is your space, make it happy, vibrant and colorful.)

Beach

Positive

Feeling light and clean

Last week happiest moment	Spent time with mom
Not so good moment	Hurt my calf while running
Something nice that someone said to you	Looking fit ☺
Something nice that you said or did for someone	Visited a children home
Something special you want to do for someone next week	surprise party for nitin
Are you happy and motivated to stay healthy and fit ? (If no mention why)	yes yes yes
A reward you want to give yourself for staying on track with your fitness goals	Reuses peanut butter cup

5) In section 3 of your personal health coach, you can fill in weekly program charts to monitor your achievements against your goals. It provides you with a simple and comparative report, week after week.

Weekly Progress

	Week 1	Week 2	Week 3
Weight	75	74.2	74
Body fat %	25.5	25.4	25.2
Blood pressure	130/95	130/95	130/92
Resting heart rate	75	75	74
Total no.of exercise days	6	5	6
Average hours of sleep per night	6	7	6

EFS MODEL OF FITNESS

What is food?

Wikipedia: Food is any substance or material, eaten to provide nutritional support for the body or for pleasure. It usually consists of substances of plant and animal origin, that contains essential nutrients such as carbohydrates, proteins, fats, vitamins and minerals, and is ingested and assimilated by an organism to produce energy, stimulate growth and maintain life.

In short, food is energy. Our bodies are energy. Our thoughts, emotions and feelings are energy. Have you even noticed how low you feel when you are sad or de-motivated? You feel lethargic, lazy and low on energy levels.

Our body cells, hair, skin and nails are energy. If we provide our body with less energy, our body does not have the ability to stimulate growth or maintain the health of our living cells. Our mental functions and emotions get affected by less or wrong food.

Food can also be poison to our bodies. The wrong food, the wrong quantity of food and combinations of food with lifestyles must all be evaluated and balanced.

We need food to live. Let's quickly look at the functions of food. It is important to understand this, so that we make balanced choices.

a) Growth - Food is the growth of the human body, what manure is to the growth of a plant. The living cells in our body multiply and regenerate all the time.

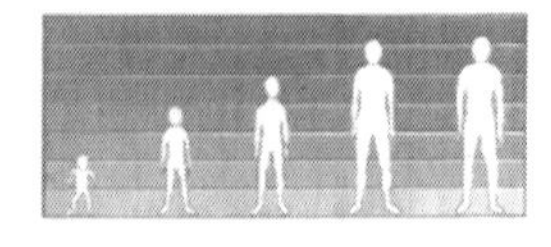

b) Repair - Our cells keep getting damaged or worn out as we grow. Pollution also damages and slowly kills our cells, which, in turn, affects the way we look and our overall health. The right kinds and amount of food can help the body repair quickly and grow.

c) Energy – We need energy to wake up, do the things we do everyday, be productive and live happy lives. As mentioned above, we are energy and this energy is provided by food and proper nutrition.

d) Protection – From diseases and infections. Food contains vitamins and minerals that make our bodies strong, and help us fight diseases, recover quickly when we are sick, help us age gracefully and prevent old age diseases in our later years.

The mantra of this book is "keep it simple", and that's exactly what I'm going to do. Now that we know why we need food, I want you to reflect on the kind and amount of food you eat on a daily basis.

Reflect back on instances when you were sick, or recovering from an injury or disease. How did your food pattern change?

We all remember our parents, loved ones or doctors telling us what to eat and what not to eat during the above mentioned situations. It is a proven fact today, that food and correct nutrition can prevent disease, alleviate conditions and also slow down the ageing process of the human body.

Diabetes, cholesterol, acidity, obesity, cardiac diseases, arthritis, cancer, in most cases, can be cured with the right kind and quantity of food you feed your body with.

Look at the kind of food a pregnant lady needs to eat. The growth of the child depends on the food that the mother eats.

"You are what you eat." I'm sure you have heard that saying before. It can be safely said that you are partly what your mother ate, as well. From the time you were a fetus, your growth depended on the quality and quantity of food that your mother consumed. Your health as a growing child depended on the foundational nutrition received when you were in the womb, and thereafter, the food you were fed while you were growing up.

- **Does your child have problems concentrating during school hours?**
- **Do you find it difficult to wake up every morning?**
- **Do you find yourself falling asleep or your eyes getting heavy during meetings at work?**
- **Do you find your ability to play a sport, dance, and trek or do physical activities decreasing?**
- **Do you find your mental power, ability to think fluctuate through the day?**
- **Do you find your irritability and anger levels rising and more difficult to control?**
- **Are you stressed?**

In most cases, in fact in almost all instances, the cause of any of the above can be traced back to the food you eat.

Mrs. Advani's son studies in the third grade in a reputed school in Mumbai. The teacher kept complaining to her that her son would constantly be sleepy through her classes and showed no interest in any sports at school.

I asked her if her son got sufficient sleep each night. "8 hours," she exclaimed. "Not an hour less. And he sleeps deeply, almost never waking up in between," she said.
"Okay, that's great" I said. "8 hours is the ideal amount of sleep a child needs. So what do you give him for breakfast?" I asked.

"A glass of milk with Horlicks. That's good right?" she quickly asked. "And when is his next meal post breakfast?" I asked. "That would be at about 10:30 am," she said.

A gap of 4 hours between breakfast and his first snack, and all that the boy had, as a source of energy to keep him awake and help him concentrate at school or play a game, was a glass of milk. Don't forget his last meal was dinner the previous night. So from then till 10:30am the next day, her son's only source of energy was a glass of milk.

No wonder Mrs. Advani's son was sleepy. His breakfast lacked a key nutrient, 'carbohydrates', that would provide him constant energy during the day. His breakfast did not have any nutritional balance.

I wrote about the rising number of restaurants and eateries across our county. Global cuisines, fine dining, buffets, grills and bistros, steak houses and numerous bakeries.

Does this mean we cannot enjoy all these options that exist? Yes you can.
The fact that there are so many options, each one more tempting than the other, and the fact that socializing is a must today, stresses out so many of my clients when it comes to making a decision of where and what to eat.

Remember our mantra. "Keep it simple." Yes, you can go out and eat at any of these joints, what's important are the choices you make and the techniques you use.

The intention of this chapter is to revive our knowledge and learn some more about food, so that we know what we can eat when we choose from the available options and improve our lifestyles and those of our families, by using this knowledge in our own homes. We will also learn how to organize our daily food plans to stay fit.

Back to School:
Carbohydrates, Proteins and Fats. The three macro nutrients. I remember this chapter in science class back at school. It is so important that we understand the function of each of these nutrients required by our body to perform different roles and actions.

As you read further, you will understand how to use each of these three macro nutrients in your daily food plans to achieve your fitness goal. Knowledge of this will empower you to make balanced choices when you must eat out, in a new country, on a holiday or at a social function.

I must emphasize that no matter what your fitness goal is, all these three macro nutrients are required for great health and you must never eliminate any of them from your nutrition plan.

Carbohydrates:
You can google up carbohydrates and you will come up with about 267000 results. But our mantra is "keep it simple" and that's what I'm going to do.

Carbohydrates provide energy to our body.

a) It enables us to do work, to move, to play, to study, to make love, to be happy, and control our emotions.

b) It promotes cell fertilization and development. Is your skin looking dull or is your hair weak? Both are made up of cells and carbohydrates provide energy to these cells to develop and grow.

c) Carbohydrates are vital for the correct functioning of our brain, heart, nervous, digestive and immune system.

d) Fiber, which is a form of carbohydrate, is essential for the elimination of waste materials and toxins from the body, keeping the intestines disease free and clean.

There are two kinds of carbohydrates.

Simple Carbohydrates – The body is able to break down these carbohydrates quickly into energy. Simply put, simple carbs are easily digested by the body.

These foods would be ideal to consume before an examination, half an hour before exercise, before a long meeting, or an interview, when you're stuck in traffic and you're tired. They give your body and brain instant energy and power.
Examples of simple carbohydrates are fruits, fruit juices, milk, yogurt, honey and sugar.

Complex Carbohydrates – The body takes longer to break down these foods into energy. Simply put, complex carbs take time for the body to digest and are usually packed with fiber, vitamins and minerals.

These foods give the body sustained energy for a longer period of time. You should usually have a breakfast rich in complex carbs to give you sustained energy through the day. This does not stop you from adding simple carbs to your breakfast either.

You should have complex carbs an hour before your workouts to provide you sustained energy for a productive workout. Students should consume complex carbs to give them energy to study through the night.

Examples of complex carbohydrates are vegetables, breads, cereals, legumes and whole grains.

Cholesterol, fat and complex carbohydrates:
Porridge, also known as oats, is a heart friendly food and you will find most nutritionists recommending this wonder food to their weight loss clients. Complex carbs digest slowly; it actually physically moves slowly through your intestines, dragging fat molecules along with it and stabilizing blood sugar levels in the body, which, in turn, are both great for maintaining healthy cholesterol levels and reducing your body fat.

So you see, one common aspect between carbs and ... is that they both provide energy, but at different levels.

It is very important that you have the right mix of carbs at the right time of the day.
It is important that I mention this here; Carbohydrates are the only nutrients that reach the brain and provide it with energy. Proteins and fats never reach the brain. It is now a known fact that if your food plan has less carbs in, you are bound to find yourself irritable, emotional and more stressed through the day, because your brain is demanding energy from the only source that can provide it energy, and it is not getting the required amount.

Carbohydrates provide the brain with energy, which is, in turn, used to produce hormones called "endorphins" which enhance the mood. Other hormones called "serotonin" that make you feel happy and "tryptophan" that help you sleep, also require "carb power" to be produced and released by the brain.

So you need carbohydrates in your food plan, simple and complex, to reach a level of fitness.

I have a client in Hong Kong. She does not need to lose weight, but she is terrified of gaining it. Great body, but she is not fit. Reflect on the definition of fitness. Didn't the definition have 'mental health' as a part of it? She does an extremely low carb diet, because she thinks carbs will make her fat. Over the years she began to experience extreme hair loss, her skin began to sag and she was depressed with an extremely short fuse to go with all of that.

I learnt about her carb deficiency in our first counseling session. The only change she had to make was to start eating more carbs in her diet.

You see, here is how it works. Keeping it simple, but you must understand this bit of body science. Our body breaks down carbs for energy. If we consume more carbs than required and the body does not need that much of energy, it converts the extra energy into "glycogen" in our liver. How big is our liver? It's small. So what happens when there's no more place for the liver to store excess energy/glucose? It gets converted to fat.

So you see, there is nothing wrong with carbs. Yes, there are carbs that should be avoided, like table sugar, syrups, fizzy drinks, refined products like white bread and so on, because these are foods that provide almost no nutritional value, and disturb the functioning of our body by spiking up sugar levels. These bad carbs get easily converted to fat.

If you consume excess protein, your body will use only what it needs, and the rest will be converted to fat.

So eat your carbs, your body needs them, but make a balanced choice of simple and complex carbs.

You got Juice?

There is a lot being said about juicing fruits. It's convenient, no doubt, quick and easy to prepare, and you can sip on it while driving to work, at a meeting, or during your workout. People see the word fruit written on a tetra pack and it goes right into their shopping cart. Some companies even advertise '100% pure juice', but there will be preservatives, which are not natural, otherwise these juice cartons should have a shelf life of less than 48 hours, before they spoiled.

Fruits are loaded with healthy natural sugars, vitamins, minerals and fiber. What happens when you put it in the mixer? The fiber gets broken down and so do most of the valuable nutrients. So is that glass of juice really doing what you expect it to do for your body?

It's still better than having carbonated drinks, but it's more effective to eat the whole fruit and reap all its nutritional benefits.

I had a client who believed that the body should digest fruit juice faster than a whole fruit. Remember, a fruit, in whole form or juice is a simple carbohydrate, and the body quickly digests both.

Now mixing a fruit juice with a vegetable is a better option than just a plain fruit juice. Vegetables are complex carbohydrates, and when put through a mixer, fiber still gets retained. So you may explore different combinations of fruits and vegetables and whip up a refreshing and healthy juice.

That's all about carbohydrates. Keep it simple, eat your carbohydrates, enjoy them too.

Protein:
Builds up, maintains and replaces the tissues in our body. They are the building blocks of life. Your muscles, organs, immune system, hair, skin, nails need protein to grow and stay healthy.

But protein cannot survive alone. It cannot perform its function alone. It needs energy to do its work, and where will it get this energy? Carbohydrates.

Let's look at the functions of protein.
a) Maintenance and healthy growth of the body.
b) Building and repairing tissues.
c) Formation of hormones and regulation of body processes.
d) Helps the body fight infections.
e) Source of energy when your body is low on carbohydrates.

Common foods rich in protein are eggs, milk, soymilk, tofu, cheese, whey, nuts, chicken and lean meat, fish, broccoli, dark green leafy vegetables and seeds.

The non-vegetarian diet is higher in protein than the vegetarian diet, but with the right quantities, choices and combinations of vegetarian options, meeting the daily-required amount of protein for the body of a vegetarian is easy.

It's funny how people today keep changing their moisturizers, shampoos and creams and yet struggle to achieve strong hair, supple and glowing skin.

Let's take the example of a plant. No matter how many chemicals you spray it with, the leaves may look green and clean, but the health of the plant is poor. Nutrition for the plant happens at and through the roots.

The external look of a plant is dependent on the nutrition its roots can sap up from the soil. You put the right manure, that's food for the plant; if you have a strong and healthy looking plant. Now this may take time. Growing is a steady and slow, but a sure process.

The health of your skin and hair depends on the food you feed your body. That's the truth and there's no debating that fact.

Look around at the array of different creams and shampoos available in the market. One would think that with all that there is to choose from, and pretty affordable too, there wouldn't be so many people struggling to fix their hair and skin.

I'm not saying stop using shampoos and creams. Use them. I use them too, but don't begin to believe that they are the solutions for better looking skin or stronger hair. The long lasting and sure solution is in the food that you eat.

Your hair and skin are protein, the "Building blocks of life" as some medical journals define them. So if you have falling or weak hair, reflect on your food habits. Of course the reason for that doesn't have to mean that you are low on protein. There are so many other factors that can cause weak hair and poor quality skin – pollution, smoking, excessive alcohol, lack of exercise, but we are keeping it simple now, and we are going to the roots. Start looking at the amount of protein rich foods you have in your diet.

The truth about Whey:
When I think or hear the word "Whey", the word misunderstood comes to my mind. There are bad things being said about whey.

Whey is left over when milk coagulates and contains everything that is soluble from milk. It is a pure form of protein.

When you hear the word 'Whey", bulging muscles or images of bodybuilders come to your mind. Did you know that pregnant women consume whey protein under directions of doctors today?

In a vegetarian diet where your sources for high quality protein are less than the choices in the non-vegetarian food group, whey is prescribed to ensure that the growing fetus and the mother get sufficient protein to enable growth and repair of body cells.

A lot of people use whey today with the goal of building muscle. It's true; whey does help you build lean mass, which is muscle. When you work out and break down muscle through exercise, your muscles need protein to repair the very minor tears in its tissues. Protein fixes these tears and that's how the muscle grows. Whey protein can have side effects when the intake is abused. I've seen people take whey protein shakes 4-5 times a day with the stupid belief that the more protein you consume, the more muscle you build.

Please be sure to read the nutritional value chart on the brand of whey that you buy. In my experience I have seen so many enthusiastic people just check one factor on the tub, the number of grams of protein per scoop of whey. You need to check the fat, sugar content, sodium and so many other things, which I will throw light on, in the coming chapters of this book.

Your body needs only a certain amount of protein. Remember what I wrote earlier. Extra protein will be stored as fat. You will put extra stress on your kidneys and liver to assimilate this extra protein that your muscles don't need.

As per medical sources, you need maximum 1 gram of protein per pound of your body weight. Professional bodybuilders and pro - athletes may consume more, because the intensity of their workouts is such that their muscles need extra protein.

Consult a sports nutritionist or your doctor. There are several misconceptions in the market today and everyone has a different view or suggestions on the amount of protein one should take.

Keeping it simple:
Excess protein will convert to fat and you will put stress on your kidneys and liver and there is ongoing research that excess protein can make your bones brittle.

Looking on the positive side, there are ongoing and strong research reports showing that whey supplements in the right quantity can regulate metabolism, prevent diseases and have anti-cancer and anti-inflammatory properties.

My suggestion would be to derive protein from your natural foods in your daily food plan and take whey under professional direction to reap maximum fitness benefits. You should try to include some protein food in every meal and snack option during the day. This will help the body maintain a uniform and highly powered metabolism as well as rejuvenate and power your body cells.

Reflect on your fitness goal. Do you really need that much of whey? TV shows, movies, magazine, "only make you feel ugly" is so true, as said by Baz Luhrman.
You must invest time in creating your fitness goal, only then can you envision how you want to look and feel, as you live each day.

FATS:

Michelle was 22 years old when we started working together on her fitness levels. When we first met, I was shocked to see her cheeks and eyes all sunken in, her hair was frizzy and her skin flaky. She was thin, not slim and she needed help to get her skin and hair in place. So I began with my questions to determine her eating habits and lifestyle. Michelle had not consumed fats for over 2 months. I was surprised she was even able to walk or do her daily chores. By the time I reached the end of my session with her, my notes told me that she had been irritable of late, getting angry for the smallest reasons, she felt depressed most of the time and was addicted to her exercise, obsessed was actually the right word to use. Her concentration levels at college were fluctuating and she was even thinking of dropping out. Her hobby? Easy guess. Was working out at the gym twice a day.

What is FAT:

Fat is a nutrient that is an important source of calories. As of now, think of a calorie as energy. One gram of fat supplies 9 calories as compared to the 4 calories produced by 1 gram of carbohydrate or protein. There are different kinds of fat, each of them having different functions to perform in our body. Fats are found in different kinds of food. Some of the fat we eat comes from the fat that we cook our food in. A lot of fat is hidden in foods that we eat as snacks, pastries and prepared meals. When we eat a lot of high fat food, we get a lot of energy. With too many calories, we may gain weight, because the body may not need so many calories to provide energy, especially if we are not physically active. These calories turn into fat. Too much fat, in turn leads to cardiovascular diseases, high blood pressure, cancer, stroke and a whole load of other health complications.

Let's have a look at the different kinds of fat and how they couple with our overall health and fitness.

Saturated Fats

These are the only kinds of fats that raise blood cholesterol levels. Saturated fats are found in meats and whole dairy products like milk, cheese, cream and ice cream. Some saturated fats are also found in plant foods like tropical oils (coconut or palm kernel oil). Butter, margarine, and fats in meat and dairy products are all especially high in saturated fat.

We can reduce the saturated fats in our diet by using skimmed milk and low fat cheese instead of whole milk and cheese. We can also use less fat, oil, butter, and margarine. At the table, use a tub of margarine instead of butter. Another way to cut down on fat is to drain and trim meats and take the skin off poultry. Simply reducing the total amount of fat we eat goes a long way toward reducing saturated fats.

Unsaturated Fats

Unsaturated fats are usually liquid at room temperature. They are found in most vegetable products and oils. An exception is a group of tropical oils like coconut or palm kernel oil, which is highly saturated.

Using foods containing "polyunsaturated" and "monounsaturated" fats do not increase our risk of heart disease. However, like all fats, unsaturated fats give us 9 calories for every gram. So eating too much of these types of fats may also make us gain weight. We can reduce the fat and unsaturated fats in our diet by using less fat, oil, and margarine. We can also eat more low-fat foods like vegetables, fruits, breads, rice, pasta and cereals.

Monounsaturated Fats

Are liquid at room temperature and turn cloudy when kept in a refrigerator. Primary sources are plant oils like canola oil, peanut oil, and olive oil. Other good sources are avocados, nuts such as almonds, hazelnuts, pecans, and seeds such as pumpkin and sesame seeds.

People following traditional Mediterranean diets, which are very high in foods containing monounsaturated fats like olive oil, tend to have lower risk of cardiovascular disease.

Polyunsaturated Fats

Are liquid at room temperatures as well as at cold temperatures. Primary sources are sunflower, corn, soybean, and flaxseed oils, and also foods such as walnuts, flax seeds, and fish.

This fat family includes the Omega-3 group of fatty acids, which are anti-inflammatory and which your body can't make. Omega-3 fats are found in very few foods and are known as "Super healthy fats" today.

We should all be increasing our intake of healthy omega-3 fatty acids, which we need for body functions like controlling blood clotting and building cell membranes in the brain. We're still learning about the many benefits of Omega-3, but research has shown this fatty acid can have a positive impact on:

- ➔ Cardiovascular disease. Epidemiologic and clinical trials have shown that omega-3 fatty acids decrease triglyceride levels, the growth rate of atherosclerotic plaque, and the risk of arrhythmias. They can slightly lower blood pressure also.

- ➔ Liver cancer. Omega-3 fatty acids may be an effective therapy for both, the treatment and prevention of human liver cancers.

- ➔ Depression. Omega-3 fatty acid reduces symptoms of depression probably because it increases gray matter in the brain.

- ➔ Dementia. Eating fatty fish, high in omega 3, lowers the likelihood of developing "silent" brain lesions that can cause memory loss or dementia.

Cholesterol

Cholesterol is an essential fat made by the liver. Many people get additional cholesterol by eating meat and dairy products. Too much dietary intake may raise blood cholesterol levels, and lead to heart disease. Cholesterol is transported through the bloodstream by lipoproteins.

Trans Fat

Trans fats is produced when liquid oil is made into a solid fat. This process is called hydrogenation. Trans fats act like saturated fats and can raise your cholesterol level. Trans fats is listed on the label, making it easier to identify these foods. Unless there is at least 0.5 grams or more of Trans fat in a food, the label can claim 0 grams. If you want to avoid as much Trans fat as possible, you must read the ingredient list on food labels. Look for words like hydrogenated oil or partially hydrogenated oil. Select foods that either do not contain hydrogenated oil or where liquid oil is listed first in the ingredient list.

Sources of Trans fat include:

- ➔ Processed foods like snacks (crackers and chips) and baked goods, (muffins, cookies and cakes) with hydrogenated oil or partially hydrogenated oil
- ➔ Stick margarines
- ➔ Shortening
- ➔ Some fast food items such as French fries

Knowing the facts about cholesterol can reduce your risk for a heart attack or stroke. But understanding what cholesterol is and how it affects your health is only the beginning.

To keep your cholesterol under control:

- ➔ Schedule a screening
- ➔ Eat foods low in cholesterol and saturated fat
- ➔ Maintain a healthy weight
- ➔ Exercise regularly
- ➔ Follow your healthcare professional's advice

While it's prudent to watch the levels of cholesterol you eat, healthy fats can actually help your body process cholesterol in a more beneficial manner. For example:

- ➔ Monounsaturated fats lower total and bad (LDL) cholesterol levels, while increasing good cholesterol (HDL).

→ Polyunsaturated fats can lower triglycerides and fight inflammation,

→ On the other hand, saturated fat can raise blood cholesterol.
Trans fats are even worse, since they not only raise bad LDL cholesterol, but also lower the good HDL cholesterol.

Why do we need fats?
Although fats have received a bad reputation for causing weight gain, some fat is essential for survival. According to the Dietary Reference Intakes published by the USDA, 20% - 35% of calories should come from fat. We need this amount of fat for:

→ **Body to use vitamins:** Vitamins A, D, E, and K are fat-soluble vitamins, meaning that the fat in foods helps the intestines absorb these vitamins into the body.

→ **Brain development:** Fat provides the structural components not only of cell membranes in the brain, but also of myelin, the fatty insulating sheath that surrounds each nerve fiber, enabling it to carry messages faster.

→ **Energy:** Gram for gram, fats is the most efficient source of food energy. Each gram of fat provides nine calories of energy for the body, compared with four calories per gram each of carbohydrates and proteins.

→ **Healthier skin:** One of the more obvious signs of fatty acid deficiency is dry, flaky skin. In addition to giving skin its rounded appeal, the layer of fat just beneath the skin acts as the body's own insulation to help regulate body temperature.

→ **Healthy cells:** Fats are a vital part of the membrane that surrounds each cell of the body. Without a healthy cell membrane, the rest of the cells can't function.

→ **Making hormones:** Fats are structural components of some of the most important substances in the body, including hormones that regulate many of the body's functions. Fats regulate the production of sex hormones, which explains why some teenage girls who are too lean experience delayed pubertal development.

→ **Pleasure:** Besides being a nutritious energy source, fat adds to the appealing taste, texture and appearance of food. Fats carry flavor.

→ **Protective cushion for our organs:** Many of the vital organs, especially the kidneys, heart, and intestines are cushioned by fat that helps protect them from injury and hold them in place.

Facts:

- ➔ Ironically, cutting fat out of our diets seems to have the opposite effect: while Americans have been eating less fat, we've been getting fatter. In place of fats, many people turn to foods full of easily digested carbohydrates, or fat-free products that replace healthy fats with sugar and high-calorie, refined carbohydrates.

- ➔ You need to cut calories to lose weight - fats are more filling and curbing hunger can stop you from indulging in additional calories.

- ➔ The 2006 Women's Health Initiative Dietary Modification Trial showed that women on low-fat diets didn't lose any more weight than women who followed their usual diets.

You need fat for optimal health and fitness levels and like carbohydrates, there are good and bad fats that we have just seen exist. Use the good fats in food plans and limit or completely eliminate the bad fats that do no good but only harm the body.

How much fat is too much?

How much fat is too much depends on lifestyle, weight, age and most importantly the state of health. The USDA recommends that the average individual:

- ➔ Keep total fat intake to 20-35% of calories
- ➔ Limit saturated fats to less than 10% of calories (200 calories for a 2000 calorie diet)
- ➔ Limit trans fats to 1% of calories (2 grams per day for a 2000 cal diet)
- ➔ Limit cholesterol to 300 mg per day

Keeping it Simple: Now you know all about good and bad fats, what you should continue to eat and what you should reduce.

So going back to Michelle's case, here's what we did. We began to re-structure her food plan, add healthy fats and a good amount of rest to her daily plan. She began to eat many of her favorite foods that she had been denying herself off over the previous months and the change was phenomenal. Her skin visibly changed over the next 3 weeks and her face began to fill up. She even reported better concentration levels and began to socialize more often with friends. She cut her workouts to once a day with two days of rest in the week. Sometimes when I reflect about this case, I think it was the addition of "the right amount of fat", in her food plan that accelerated this change.

Fat is not your enemy. You may be skeptical when I say, "Fat burns Fat." Consuming the right fats in the right quantities will help power your metabolism, which, in turn, will help you lose weight and maintain a healthy fat percentage in your body composition. Dietary fats supply some of the best and most stable sources of energy.

So if you want to feel good all day long, you need to make sure you are getting enough fats, and the right types.

The human body needs fat just to function properly, let alone optimal health. Certain amounts of fat are necessary for proper hormone production. If hormone production is off, your metabolism will also be off. Hormones regulate many things in the body including your ability to build and maintain muscle tissue, which is responsible for a large portion of your energy expenditure. In simple terms, muscle burns calories 24 hours a day and if you eat a low fat or no fat diet you will have a hard time building and maintaining muscle.

We have just covered three macronutrients. I must remind you that the mantra of this book is "keeping it simple." You can google the above subject and learn so much more, but don't let all of that confuse you to an extent that it makes it difficult to even start doing the basics. The idea is "starting to do."

Micronutrients: are nutrients needed by the body throughout life, in small quantities. They are dietary minerals and vitamins needed by the body in very small quantities as opposed to macronutrients that are required in larger amounts.

Examples of minerals are iron, cobalt, zinc, selenium, copper, chromium, manganese and molybdenum.

The human body cannot make vitamins. Therefore we must obtain them from the food we eat.

Vitamins and minerals are substances that are found in the foods we eat. Your body needs them to work properly, so you grow and develop just like you should. When it comes to vitamins, each one has a special role to play. For example:

Vitamin D in milk helps your bones.

Vitamin A in carrots helps you see at night.

Vitamin C in oranges helps your body heal if you get a cut.

B vitamins in leafy green vegetables help your body make protein and energy.

Vitamins Hang Out in Water and Fat

There are two types of vitamins: fat soluble and water-soluble. When you eat foods that contain fat-soluble vitamins, the vitamins are stored in the fat tissues in your body and in your liver. They wait around in your body fat until your body needs them.

Fat-soluble vitamins are happy to stay stored in your body for a while - some stay for a few days, some for up to 6 months! Then, when it's time for them to be used, special carriers in your body take them to where they're needed. Vitamins A, D, E, and K are all fat-soluble vitamins.

Water-soluble vitamins are different. When you eat foods that have water-soluble vitamins, the vitamins don't get stored as much in your body. Instead, they travel through your bloodstream. Whatever your body doesn't use gets excreted.

So these kinds of vitamins need to be replaced often because they don't stick around! This crowd of vitamins includes vitamin C and the big group of B vitamins - B1 (thiamin), B2 (riboflavin), niacin, B6 (pyridoxine), folic acid, B12 (cyanocobalamin), biotin, and pantothenic acid.

Now let's have a look at the different kinds of vitamins and the non vegetarian and vegetarian food sources you can obtain these from.

Your Vitamin Chart

Vitamin	Benefits	Food Source (veg)	Food Source (non-veg)
A	Vitamin A prevents eye problems, promotes a healthy immune system, is essential for the growth and development of cells, and keeps skin healthy.	Fortified cereals, carrots, sweet potatoes, pumpkin, kale, orange, apricots, peaches, mangoes, papayas, cantaloupe, red and yellow bell peppers.	Milk, Egg, Liver
C	Vitamin C is needed to form collagen, a tissue that helps to hold cells together. It's essential for healthy bones, teeth, gums, and blood vessels. It helps the body absorb iron and calcium, aids in wound healing, and contributes to brain function.	Red berries, kiwi fruit, red and green bell peppers, tomatoes, broccoli, spinach, guava, grapefruit, sweet lime, orange	
D	Vitamin D strengthens bones because it helps the body absorb bone-building calcium.	"Fortified milk.This vitamin is unique — your body manufactures it when you get sunlight on your skin!"	Egg yolk, Fish Oils
E	Vitamin E is an antioxidant and helps protect cells from damage. It is also important for the health of red blood cells.	Vegetable oils, nuts, green leafy vegetables, avocados, wheat germ, whole grains	
B12	Vitamin B12 helps to make red blood cells, and is important for nerve cell function.	Milk, cheese, fortified cereals.	Fish, Red meat, Poultry, Milk, Cheese, Eggs

Your Vitamin Chart

Vitamin	Benefits	Food Source (veg)	Food Source (non-veg)
B6	Vitamin B6 is important for the brain and nerves to function normally. It also helps the body break down proteins and make red blood cells.	Potatoes, bananas, beans, seeds, nuts, spinach, fortified cereals.	Red meat, Poultry, Fish, Eggs.
B1 (Thiamin)	Thiamin helps the body convert carbohydrates into energy and is necessary for the heart, muscles, and nervous system to function properly.	Fortified bread, cereals, pasta, dried beans, soya foods, peas, whole grains, wheat germ	Meat, Fish.
B2 (Riboflavin)	Riboflavin is essential for turning carbohydrates into energy and producing red blood cells. It is also important for vision.	Peas, lentils, nuts, milk, cheese, green leafy vegetables, broccoli, asparagus, fortified cereals	Meat, Eggs
B3 (Niacin)	Niacin helps the body turn food into energy. It helps maintain healthy skin and is important for nerve function.	Fortified cereals, peanuts.	Red meat, Poultry, Fish
B9 (Folate)	Folate helps the body make red blood cells. It is also needed to make DNA	Dried beans, legumes, green leafy vegetables, asparagus, oranges, citrus fruits, bread, noodles, cereals	Poultry
K	Vitamin K is fat soluble and plays a critical role in blood clotting. It regulates blood calcium levels and activates at least 3 proteins involved in bone health.	Avocado, pears, plums, blackberries, cranberries, grapes, kiwi, tomato, pomegranate, alfalfa, asparagus, cauliflower, carrots, celery, broccoli, pine nuts, cashews, pistas, bok choy, cucumber	Beef, cheese, eggs, lamb, soy milk, turkey, duck
B5 (pantothenic acid)	Pantothenic acid is essential for the metabolism of food as well as in the formation of hormones and (good) cholesterol.	Oats, rye, sunflower seeds, whole wheat, Avocado, pears, plums, blackberries, cranberries, grapes, kiwi, tomato, pomegranate, alfalfa, asparagus, cauliflower, carrots, celery, broccoli, pine nuts, cashews, pistas, bok choy, cucumber	Beef, chicken, fish, salmon, tuna, cow milk

Look closely at the types of food that are rich in the different vitamins. They are carbohydrates, proteins or fats. You will be including most of these foods in the right proportion so as to get a balanced intake of macro and micronutrients.

We need macro and micronutrients to live a fit and healthy life. Now that you know the functions of all these food groups, do you think we should be neglecting any of these nutrients from our system? Should we be avoiding or missing out on foods that will fuel our bodies with vitamins?

So how much of what, is the question that must be running across your mind now.

There are so many diets out in the market today. It's getting complicated and people are confused. Which diet should they choose? Are there side effects? Will the diet produce the desired results? How expensive will this diet be?

I must encourage you to start off by reviewing your current food plan first. Are you getting all of the macro and micronutrients? In most experiences gained through counseling and coaching, I have learnt that people who diet and keep changing their plans, never really had a balanced food plan in the first place. So we need to get things right, before we venture into the 'glamorous' world of diets and fads. Let me introduce you to the "Food Pyramid".

Food Pyramid:
The Food Pyramid is an excellent tool to help you make healthy food choices. The food pyramid can help you choose from a variety of foods so you get the nutrients you need, and the suggested serving sizes can help you control the amount of calories, fat, saturated fat, cholesterol, sugar or sodium in your diet.

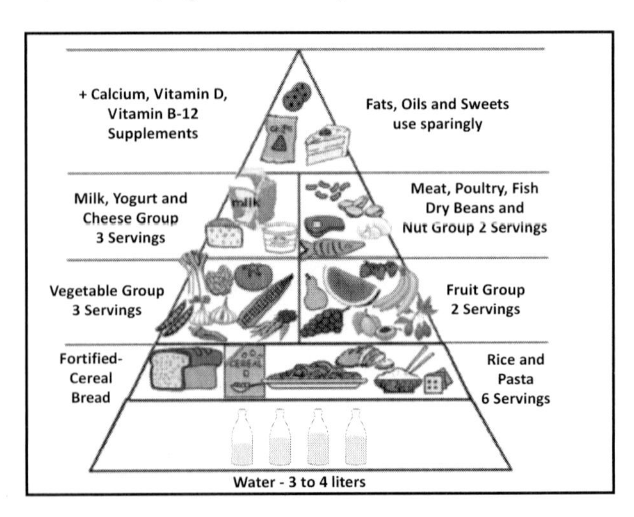

Remember, no one food can make you healthy. Eat a varied selection of foods from every level of the food pyramid. Each of the basic food groups supplies different nutrients, vitamins and minerals, giving your body the healthy nutrition needed.

Use this beautiful tool to plan your meals. A food pyramid arranges the food starting from the high calorie food at the top to the low calorie food at the base. The ideal food pyramid differs from person to person. There are different food pyramids for different people. The food pyramid for a diabetic patient will surely vary from the food pyramid of a heart patient and that goes the same for a pregnant woman and a normal person. In today's world, the demand for the food pyramid is gradually increasing, particularly in the corporate and software industry where people cannot follow a healthy routine due to their hectic work schedule. This lack of fixed routine has enhanced the demand of the food pyramids.

With the recent emphasis on weight control, the demand for food pyramid has also increased.

Have a look at the food pyramid image. You see the word serving at the side of each partition in the triangle. Each serving depicts a certain quantity of food. We will refer to a serving as a fistful. Keep it simple. Universally, one serving is measured as a fistful. It is easy to calculate and this reference comes in hand when you do not have a measuring cup or a scale handy.

What you will also observe is that all foods mentioned in the pyramid, are made up of carbs, proteins fats, and contain vitamins and minerals. By just applying this concept to when designing your food plan, you automatically ensure a balanced diet.

Are you getting your quota of nutrients in your daily food plan?
I strongly suggest you take a print out of this pyramid, and fix it on your kitchen wall or fridge door. It ensures that you eat a balanced meal everyday. It may suddenly strike you now, that maybe you have not been eating a balanced meal everyday. Just by making these changes, you can start losing weight and shaping up, because in most cases, when we eat or cook randomly, our meals tend to be too heavy on carbs and fats, or in some cases too heavy on protein. It needs to be balanced so that we give our body all the nutrients it needs, in the right quantities, to do it's job, and, in turn, make us feel and look good.

Calories:
"That's loaded with calories!"
"Are you counting your calories?"

When people talk about the calories in food, what do they mean? A calorie is a unit of measurement - but it doesn't measure weight or length. A calorie is a unit of energy. When you hear something contains 100 calories, it's a way of describing how much energy your body could get from eating or drinking it.

Are Calories Bad for You?
Calories aren't bad for you. Your body needs calories for energy. But eating too many calories - and not burning enough of them off through activity - can lead to weight gain.

Most foods and drinks contain calories. Some foods, such as lettuce, contain few calories. (A cup of shredded lettuce has less than 10 calories.) Other foods, like peanuts, contain a lot of calories. (Half a cup of peanuts has 427 calories.)

You can find out how many calories are there in a food by looking at the nutrition facts label. It will also describe the components of the food - how many grams of carbohydrate, protein, and fat it contains. Here's how many calories are there in 1 gram of each:

- Carbohydrate - 4 calories
- Protein - 4 calories
- Fat - 9 calories

That means if you know how many grams of each one are in a food, you can calculate the total calories. You would multiply the number of grams by the number of calories in a gram of that food component. For example, if a serving of potato chips (about 20 chips) has 10 grams of fat, 90 calories are from fat. That's 10 grams * 9 calories per gram.

That's how simple it is to understand calories. You will find that I use this term through the rest of the book, so please ensure you read the above again so that you have a clear understanding of the term.

All About Metabolism:
You hear this word all the time these days. “He's got a fast metabolism, that's why he's always so fit.” “I need to increase my metabolism,” “I'm fat because I was born with a low metabolism.”

But what is metabolism? How does it play a role in your weight loss goals and what is its value to you? Let me give you the commonly accepted definition of metabolism.

The word metabolism is derived from the Greek language, and it means "change" or "transformation". For our purposes of body function, metabolism is the amount of energy or calories your body burns to maintain vital functions. At every moment, be it sleeping, shopping or exercising, your body is constantly burning calories. It needs fuel just as a car needs fuel to power itself. Your metabolism is the regulator and manager of your body's fuel.

Now here's where it really gets interesting. Your metabolism is affected by your body composition. In plain English, this means the amount of muscle or lean mass you have compared to the amount of fat you have on your body. This comparison is important because your muscle tissue burns or uses up more calories to maintain itself than fat does. People who have a lot of muscle on them or mostly muscle on their frame, tend to have a higher metabolism than others who have more fat. So why should this matter to you?

Consider this:

Take two people who have the same height and weight. Let's say one exercises on a regular basis with weights plus she does aerobic exercises and she has a low percentage of body fat. The other woman never exercises and has more fat on her frame. The first woman will have a higher metabolism than the second one. Because of this, the first woman will find it much easier to maintain her figure and will not add on much fat to her body. However the second woman will find that she is gaining more fat and consequently weight gain will come much easier, and that's why her weight will balloon at a much faster pace.

Ask yourself this question:

Which woman would you rather be? By now you're probably wondering how you could increase your metabolic rate. That's a good question.

It's important to note that some people were born with a faster metabolism than others. That's why they can eat and eat some more, and they rarely gain any weight while other people are hard-wired for a slower metabolism.

I'm going to break this down once again. It is important that you must understand this term, as metabolism is really your regulator and manager of your body's food.

Your metabolism is the speed at which your body produces energy. How does your body produce energy? It produces energy by burning calories, by breaking down your food through digestion.

If you feed your body 10 grams of carbohydrates, that is 10 grams X 4 (1 gram of carb gives 4 calories of energy) = 40 calories.

The faster your metabolism, the faster your body does everything, including burning fat. Some indicators that your metabolism is improving or getting faster and better are:

a) You find your fingernails growing faster.
b) Your hair growing faster
c) Energy levels soar through the day
d) You cheat on junk food, your weight does not increase a bit
e) You have more energy during your workouts.
f) You find that if you miss your workout, you feel lethargic and uneasy.
g) Your body requires food every 2.5 to 3 hours and it will remind you by making your tummy growl or have a rippling feeling every 2.5 to 3 hours.

So to improve your metabolism here is what you must focus on.

Eat small meals every 2.5 to 3 hours:

When you sleep, your metabolism slows down considerably. That's why when you wake up, you feel groggy and lazy at times. You need food; you need fuel to kick-start your metabolism and, in turn, get your body mechanism started. So you have breakfast. Your metabolism soars. If your next meal is lunch and thereafter dinner, the gap between each meal is too large. You will see slumps in your metabolism. The body metabolism will not be uniform through the day, which is why some people experience low energy levels and fatigue at certain times in the day. It's a great habit to start eating every 2.5 to 3 hours. Why this specific time? Because it usually takes your digestive system approximately this time to completely digest your food or snack. So by the time the digestion is done, instead of keeping an empty stomach, you feed more food to your body, which means more energy, higher metabolism and high levels of energy. Plus you actually maintain a healthy weight and lose weight, because calories are burned by your body (metabolism) during the digestion process. When you eat every 2.5 to 3 hours you will find that your portion size at lunch and dinner will cut down considerably. This is because you will not be that hungry. Since you have small snacks during the day, your digestion will be uniform, and remember, the smaller your meals, the more efficient is your digestion, leaving little or no chance for food to get converted to fat and stored in your body.

Exercise:

One of the best ways to naturally boost your metabolism is exercise. This topic will be discussed in detail, in the next section of this book.

Never skip meals:

Never skip meals. Your body metabolism will slow down. In fact a gauge to check if your metabolism is improving is the practice of eating every 2.5 to 3 hours. After practising this lifestyle change for 2 weeks, try missing a snack. Your tummy will growl and grumble to remind you that it's time for its fuel supply, and you will have to eat something, because this is a feeling which will be hard to ignore or push aside. Once you experience this, then you know that your body has been conditioned, and it's a sign that your metabolism is on the rise.

When you skip meals, you put your body into "famine" mode and your body naturally stores your next meal as fat, in expectation of a recurring "famine". To lose weight, you must eat.

Never skip Breakfast. Make it the largest meal of your day:

When you wake up, your body is like the cold engine of a car. It needs to be warmed up to start. Your metabolism is the same. It needs to be jump-started. Once your metabolism is at optimum levels, your bodily functions perform efficiently. Breakfast is that source of fuel. If you skip your breakfast, your body has really not woken up and you start your day on a tired note, physically or mentally or both. What happens next is predictable. Your lunch portion will be huge, because you have no fuel source since the previous night's dinner.

Breakfast will kick-start your metabolism and set the course of your day. Most people who skip breakfast have weight related problems. In many countries, you will be served chocolate pastries, Danish pastries and other savory items for breakfast. Too much of these pastries may not be a health choice, but guess what, if you eat them at breakfast, you have the entire day for your body to break it down, with very little chances of it getting stored as fat, considering you have an active day ahead of you and will do some sort of exercise.

I'd like to mention here about the importance of starting your day with fruits. If you go back to the carbohydrate section in the book, fruits are categorized as a "simple" carbohydrate. Which simply means, that a fruit gets digested quickly by the body, providing instant energy to the individual consuming it.

Many of us must have that cup of tea or coffee upon waking up. Nothing wrong with that; the only suggestion being, have your piece of fruit first. Let the instant energy jump start our metabolism, and then have your tea and coffee. Tea or coffee stimulates the brain to wake up, but it suppresses your metabolism. What you want is a complete wake up. A fruit will help you do that, and then if you must, enjoy your cuppa.

Drink water:

Drink water through the day. I cannot emphasize how important this is for your metabolism. Water makes up more than two thirds of the weight of the human body, and without it, we would die in a few days. The human brain is made up of 95% water, blood is 82% and air 90%. A mere 2% drop in our body's water supply can trigger signs of dehydration: fuzzy short-term memory, trouble with basic math, and difficulty focusing on smaller print, such as a computer screen. (Are you having trouble reading this? Drink up!) Mild dehydration is also one of the most common causes of daytime fatigue. An estimated seventy-five percent of Americans have mild, chronic dehydration – a pretty scary statistic for a developed country where water is readily available through the tap or bottle.

Water is important to the mechanics of the human body. The body cannot work without it, just as a car cannot run without gas and oil. In fact, all the cell and organ functions made up in our entire anatomy and physiology depend on water for their functioning.

- ➔ Water serves as a lubricant
- ➔ Water forms the base for saliva
- ➔ Water forms the fluids that surround the joints
- ➔ Water regulates the body temperature, as the cooling and heating is distributed through perspiration
- ➔ Water helps to alleviate constipation by moving food through the intestinal tract and thereby eliminating waste- the best detox agent
- ➔ Water regulates metabolism

In addition to the daily maintenance of our bodies, water also plays a key role in the prevention of disease. Drinking eight glasses of water daily can decrease the risk of colon cancer by 45%, bladder cancer by 50% and it can potentially even reduce the risk of breast cancer. And those are just a few examples! Drinking water should always be clean and free of contaminants to ensure proper health and wellness.

If your workplace or home is air-conditioned, all the more reason for you to be aware of the amount of water you drink. When in an air-conditioned environment, you don't usually feel thirsty; even though your body may be dehydrating, you don't feel it, because of the climate. That's why you must make a conscious effort to drink up. Fill up three 1-liter bottles. Keep two of them at work, and ensure those two bottles are over before you leave for home, and ensure the third one is over before you end your day. It's the best way to track the water you drink. If you are involved in sports or any exercise, increase your intake to compensate for the water lost through sweat.

Don't avoid Fats in your food plan:

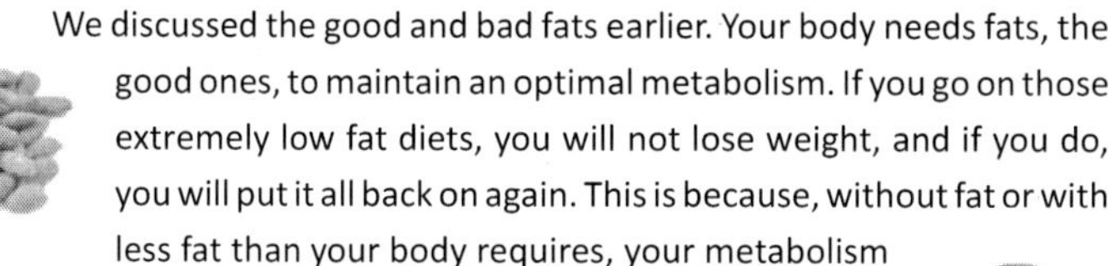

We discussed the good and bad fats earlier. Your body needs fats, the good ones, to maintain an optimal metabolism. If you go on those extremely low fat diets, you will not lose weight, and if you do, you will put it all back on again. This is because, without fat or with less fat than your body requires, your metabolism will be low, and by now you know the importance of having a great metabolism. Eat your good fats and ensure you have a 30% intake, or as suggested by your doctor or nutritionist. It will vary from person to person depending on his or her goal and current statistics. Choose healthy fats like nuts, avocados, peanut butter, olive oil, and flax.

Why sugar is your enemy:

A lot of people keep thinking that if they cut out fat from their diet, their weight loss will be faster and they will achieve levels of fitness. Fat is required by the body for a variety of functions. And again, there are good fats and bad fats.

Sugar is your enemy. A little sugar will not do you harm, because your body will burn it to produce energy, provided you are creating a situation for your body to burn that (exercise, physical activity).

Sugar is an empty calorie. Empty calories are foods that provide high amounts of energy with very little or zero nutritional value.

Sugar that does not get broken down by the body will be converted to fat. All our ancestors and generations have been consuming sugar on a daily basis, and so a whole new argument can stem out of that.

What we must keep in mind is that they were far more active than we are today, plus they did not have an array of sugar laden products that line the shelves of our supermarkets and grocery stores today.

Cookies, soft drinks, juices, breakfast cereals, yogurts, flavored milks, pastries, savory items, chips, tomato ketchup, jams, and the list goes on.

We have all of that available today and most of the above constitute some percentage of our daily food plan.

Sugar raises our blood sugar levels rapidly. This is bad as it causes an imbalance in our sugar levels, and can lead to diabetes, heart disease, high-blood pressure, obesity and weight gain.

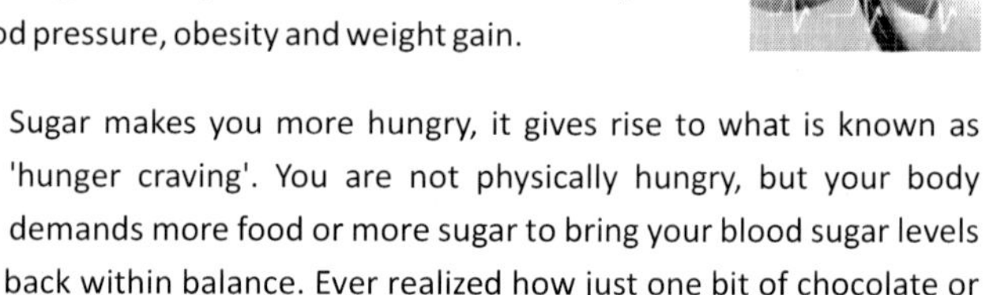

Sugar makes you more hungry, it gives rise to what is known as 'hunger craving'. You are not physically hungry, but your body demands more food or more sugar to bring your blood sugar levels back within balance. Ever realized how just one bit of chocolate or sweet is never enough? Drink a carbonated drink and you will feel the hunger craving set in within 20 - 30 minutes.

Sugar weakens your collagen. Simply put, it makes your skin look dull and loose, gives rise to wrinkles and creases in the skin. This is caused by the "free radical" (bad for your body), that excess sugar in your body produces.

Sugar is of no use to our body. I'm talking about white, refined, table sugar. Get the required, healthy sugars for your body, from natural foods that are rich in sugar, like

Fruits

Vegetables

Honey

Jaggery

Make an attempt to cut down your sugar intake today. It's a lifestyle change. Reduce your intake day by day.

Have a little, but make sure you do your exercise to burn or break down that sugar, so it does not get stored away as fat in your body.

You can't say NO to all pastries, desserts or foods that contain sugar, but you can reduce your intake and ensure you do your bit of exercise.

You know you can do it, so you only need to start.

Antioxidants:

Antioxidants are phytochemicals, vitamins and other nutrients that protect our cells from damage caused by free radicals. Studies have shown that antioxidants help prevent the free radical damage that is associated with cancer and heart disease. Antioxidants can be found in most fruits and vegetables but some culinary and medicinal herbs also contain high levels of antioxidants.

So what is a free radical? It's important you know this, as it is free radicals that cause most of the diseases today, like cancer, cardiac diseases and so on.

Free radicals are formed as part of our natural metabolism but also by environmental factors, including smoking, pesticides, pollution and radiation. These are unstable molecules that change the stability, or simply put, the health of our cells. They damage our cells and eventually kill them. Most diseases and ageing are caused by the slow damage or death of our body cells.

Antioxidants have the property to neutralize free radicals. However, when the antioxidant neutralizes a free radical it becomes inactive. Therefore we need to continuously supply our body with antioxidants. The action of free radicals could increase the risk of diseases such as cancer and heart problems and could accelerate ageing. Antioxidants have the property to neutralize the free radicals and prevent damage.

Antioxidants are present in many of our commonly available foods. Foods rich in vitamin C and E are especially loaded with antioxidants.

Benefits of Antioxidants:

➔ Protect the heart
➔ Reduce the risk of diseases, including cancer
➔ Slow down ageing
➔ Reduce inflammation (prevent or ease arthritis)
➔ Burn body fat
➔ Regulate metabolism
➔ Lower cholesterol and high blood pressure
➔ Keep the skin healthy and glowing

Antioxidants and Vitamin Rich Foods

Fruits	Vegetables	Spices	Whole grains	Misc	Nuts	Seeds	Lentils
Grapefruit	Broccoli	Cloves	Cereals	Green tea	Almonds	Watermelon	Green gram
Cherry	Soy	Cinnamon	Brown rice	Black tea	Walnuts	Pumkin	Kidney beans
Black berries	Tomatoes	Oregano	Bulgar wheat	Green tea and ginger	Apricots	Sunflower	Black beans/gram
Blue Berries	Kale	Turmeric	Daliya	Green teas with sesame seeds	Dates	Flax	All dals
Strawberries	Ginger		Cous Cous	Black Coffee	Prunes		Moong
Raspberries	Garlic		Quinoa		Peanuts		Soya beans
Kiwi	Spinach		Jowar		Pecans		
Red grapes	Carrot		Bajra				
Peaches			Soya flour				
Nectarines			Whole wheat				
Bananas			Oats				
Pomogranate			Barley				
Figs							
Apple							

Commonly available foods, right? We will explore how to add this to our daily food plans a little later.

Important organs of the body:
Each of our organs has different functions to perform, to keep us alive and healthy. I find it important to discuss a few of these, so you understand how they contribute to weight loss and fitness levels.

I have a client in Zurich. He plays tennis daily, eats vegetarian food only, drinks wine occasionally, but smokes at least 4 cigarettes a day. He was alarmed when he found his body fat percentage on the rise. He increased his physical activity, added resistance training to his daily routine and dropped the wine completely. When he finally did his liver function test, the doctor expressed that his liver was under stress, and slightly enlarged. To put it simply, his liver was working in overdrive to clean his body of toxins produced by his smoking habit. It was then that we learnt the importance of the liver and it's role in weight gain.

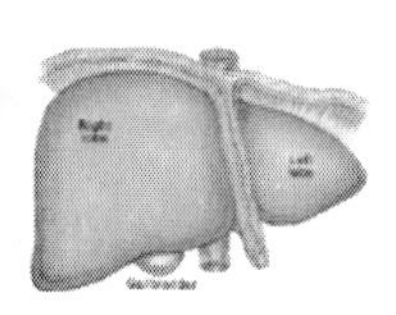

The Liver:
I will keep this as simple as possible. Without the liver, we cannot live. The liver plays a major role in metabolism, detoxification of the body, that is the removal of toxins caused by some of the foods we eat (junk food), the polluted air we breathe, medicines, recreational drugs, hard drugs, alcohol and smoking. The liver is required to produce bile that is needed for efficient digestion, it stores energy and it helps in the metabolization or break down of FAT.

The doctor explained my client's problem beautifully. Besides all the other functions of the liver, the two main functions are the filtering of toxins and the break down of fat. Now when the human body has high levels of toxins (in my client's case, these high levels were caused by his smoking), the liver works in overdrive to clean out these toxins, which otherwise, would lead to destruction of other organs and cells, and eventually death. So it stops doing its other job of breaking down fat.

That's why it's good to detoxify your body regularly. Help your liver by eating the right foods; producing fewer toxins so that your liver can also do its other functions. A healthy liver will result in a healthy weight. It's always a great idea to do a liver function test at least twice a year, considering changing lifestyles and pollution.

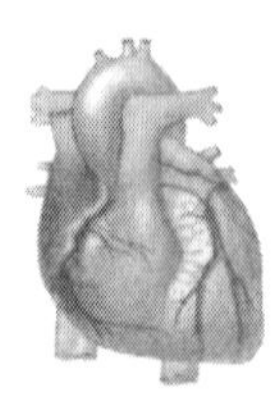

The Heart:
Without this organ, there would be no life. The heart is actually a muscle. Think of it as a pump. It pumps blood through our body and it receives the impure blood as well. Blood carries oxygen and nutrients to all the cells of our body. If the heart cannot pump effectively, some cells receive less oxygen and nutrients, leading to the destruction of these cells, the onset of diseases, strokes and paralytic attacks. That's why we need to make sure we keep our heart strong. We need to keep the veins and arteries clean so that blood can easily pass through them. If they get clogged, the heart has to work harder to pump blood through them. This weakens the heart and can even cause damage to the arteries and veins. That's why we have to be conscious of the foods that cause heart problems and we need to exercise to make this important muscle stronger.

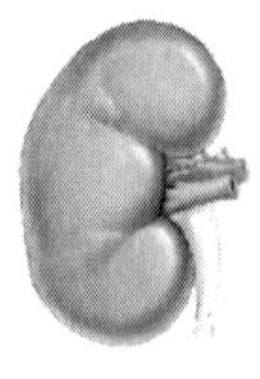

The Kidneys:
These paired structures are an essential part of the urinary system. They regulate the electrolytes in our system, maintain the acid base balance and regulate blood pressure. The kidneys serve as a natural filter of blood.

Eating the right foods along with regular exercise maintains the health of our kidneys. A food plan rich in green leafy vegetables and low in salt will ensure efficient functioning. Drinking water in the right quantities is really important as this helps the kidneys function and flush out excess toxins.

It is important to know the functions of these vital organs so you know how beneficial good food is to the human body.

Other Foods:
There are various other foods rich in iron, fiber, folic acid and the list goes on. If you maintain a balanced food plan, using the food pyramid to plan your meals, you will automatically get all the macro and micronutrients in your food plan. This is what a balanced diet is, and this is exactly how you will maintain fitness levels and a healthy weight.

Putting it all together:
For this exercise, all you need is a piece of paper and a pencil or an excel spreadsheet. Based on all that we know about food, we are going to create our own food plan. This will be a basic food plan structure. By the time you finish this book, you will be empowered on how to change this basic food plan to adapt to your fitness goals or your current state of being. What's important is getting the structure right. This will be a lifestyle change that you can aim for.

Time	Food Plan	Notes
Upon waking-up	One glass lukewarm water with a few drops of sour lime, one whole fruit or a piece of fruit	Jumpstart your metabolism and clean your liver
	Drink Water	
Breakfast	Oats with milk OR Whole grain toast OR high fiber cereal with milk OR eggs with toast OR upma, idlis, poha. (Indian cereals and grains)	
	Drink Water	
2.5 hours later	5-7 almonds plus a fruit plus a herbal tea.	If hungry add cucumber sticks
	Drink Water	
Lunch	Rotis, veggies, dal with low fat curd OR chicken, fish grilled with veggies with a serving of brown rice	
	Drink Water	
2.5 hours later	A fruit with 2 walnuts plus a yogurt if hungry. Tea can also be consumed.	
	Drink Water	
2.5 hours later	Hummus and pita bread or homemade khakra or a plain Bhel without sev, with chopped veggies. (Bhel: Puffed Rice) (Khakra: Rosted Bread)	
	Drink Water	
Dinner	Salad, soup, grilled cottage cheese with veggies or grilled non veg dish with veggies.	Baking is also a healthy way of cooking.
	Drink Water	
Before Sleep	120 ml milk or a date	

Now this is just a food plan structure. It is not made as per your goal or your weight - loss target. It is a structure for you to focus on how you should compile your own food plan.

Observe the time periods between meals. It's 2.5 to 3 hours, to keep your metabolism and energy levels up through the day.

Each main meal has choices from the food pyramid, and compiled with the mid snacks, you have a balanced food plan. Just by following this structure you can maintain healthy weight.

Alternatives are in plenty, for every meal and every food choice. Oil and sugar should be used sparingly through the day.

If you must eat out or travel, follow the same structure. This application is a lifestyle change and after 7 days of consciously following it, it will grow on you and become a habit.

That's how simple it is. You know everything you need to know about food and the way your body uses it. Put your favorite food into this structure and you have a daily food plan. Couple this with the next 2 chapters of this book, and your fitness journey has begun.

Emotional Eating:
Most of you will smile when you see the topic of this chapter. "Emotional eating". It's something almost all humans do. Some of us eat even when not hungry, when we are happy, some do it when they are sad, a lot of us do it when we are angry, depressed, hurt, bored or nervous.

Emotional eating, simply put, is eating when we are not hungry, to satisfy or fill a void. There are psychology books available in the market to address these problems, counseling and coaching sessions available to help people combat emotional eating. The issue is that large.

Yes, it is a serious problem, because it is emotional eating that leads to weight gain, obesity and a whole load of medical complications. And to make it worse, when you eat out of emotion, your choices of food are surely not going to be fruits and salads, but junk food, food rich in sugar which produce happy feelings, which raise your blood sugar levels quickly, giving you an energy rush.

For emotional eaters, food is the best friend to boost spirits, calm stress and alleviate boredom.

But according to the August issue of Mayo Clinic Women's HealthSource, emotional eating often leads to eating too much, especially high-calorie, sweet, salty and fatty foods. Women are especially prone to emotional eating -- and then feel guiltier and less healthy than men do after snacking on "forbidden" foods.

The connection between stress and eating likely has roots in brain chemistry. Faced with a real threat, the fight-or-flight reaction kicks in and suppresses appetite temporarily. But when faced with persistent stress -- health problems, difficult relationships or too much work -- many people turn to high-fat, high-calorie foods for comfort. Using food as a coping strategy doesn't alleviate stress and will likely cause weight gain.

Mayo Clinic Women's HealthSource offers these suggestions to understand and overcome emotional eating:

➔ Learn to recognize true hunger: A craving for chips or cookies soon after a meal is more likely to be emotional hunger, not real hunger.

➔ Identify the food triggers: Keeping a journal can help identify patterns in emotional eating, including emotions and feelings when eating; what and how much was eaten; and feelings after eating.

➔ Look elsewhere for comfort: Instead of grabbing a candy bar, take a walk, call a friend, listen to music, read or treat yourself to a movie.

➔ Manage stress in a healthy way: The goal is to lower stress with healthy strategies, including regular exercise, adequate rest and support from friends and family.

➔ Practice mindful eating: Mindfulness is a way of paying focused attention without judgment. Applied to eating, this technique can help increase awareness of the sensations, feelings and thoughts connected with food and eating.

➔ Toss out the unhealthy foods: Avoid stocking the cupboard or refrigerator with high-calorie comfort foods. Consider more healthful comfort foods: a bowl of tomato soup or a cup of tea.

➔ Eat a balanced diet and healthy snacks: Between meals, opt for low-fat, low-calorie snacks such as fresh fruit and unbuttered popcorn.

(Source: Mayo Clinic)

Emotional eating also stems back to the way we were brought up and the way we understood the purpose of food. I would like to share with you two articles, written by Kathy Leach, a UKCP registered Psychotherapist, specializing in overweight therapy.

Was food used as a punishment or a treat? If so, what sort of food?

Children are often 'trained to obey' with food. If the child is good, he or she will generally get rewards in food, in the form of sweets, crisps, chocolates and other goodies. If the child is naughty, then the food or treats are often withdrawn.

We need food to nourish our bodies, to stay healthy and grow. When food is used in other ways, we can lose sight of its major purpose. Of course it is pleasurable to share food, make special dishes and to have social events around food, but the important thing is to get it all into perspective.

If you sometimes yearn for those extras, what do you tell yourself? Do you think you are treating or rewarding yourself?

Do you yearn for foods that were treats in your childhood? Or do you yearn for the things that were not given to you if you were thought to have been naughty?

Then ask yourself how important they are now for you, if you think about yourself clearly as a grown-up that you are. You might be surprised how these methods of control from the past still affect you.

You must find your way to combat emotional eating. The simplest solution is by being aware. Everytime you find yourself about to eat something that is not healthy, pause for a moment. Try and analyse what you are feeling at that moment. Are you angry, sad, happy, bored? Then instead of turning to food, try and do something that makes you happy or diverts your attention, like playing a game, reading a book, watching a movie, and keep doing this everytime you feel that way. It's difficult and you will fail a couple of times, but then it will eventually become a habit, and you will learn to turn away from emotional eating.

There are several other ways for you to find things that make you happy, and food may not be the best choice. Some people I know just 'Breathe through it'.

Her name is Shinelle and she works with a large garment firm in Hongkong. Whenever she is under work pressure, she reaches out for the largest starbucks Frappe and a doughnut with sugar sprinkles. She did this month after month until she woke up one night unable to breathe and full of panic. She was admitted to the emergency room and later learnt that due to her accumulated fat, she had high blood pressure and hypertension.

When we first met, I learnt that Shinelle's food habits through the day were great. She surely had to increase her exercise from one 45 minute walk a week to three or four more. She ate healthy meals, but she fell into the trap when her job pressure rose, and that happened almost every evening, as she tallied the shipments that had to go out to over 35 countries every evening.

She was advised to start yoga and her instructor shared this bit of wisdom with her. Everytime you feel like eating junk, close your eyes, and breathe. Take in deep breaths and focus on your inhalation and exhalation. Do this until the feeling passes and most of the time, guess what, the feeling passes!

Managing stress can go a long way in maintaining healthy eating habits. In a stress packed world, sugar products and daintily decorated pastries catch the eyes of a stressed out human, triggering off attraction and want for a sugar rush. Each of us needs to consciously work to overcome this temptation.

Good luck on your journey with food.

Exercise:
What can improve your mood, boost your ability to fend off infection, and lower your risk for heart disease, diabetes, high blood pressure, and colon cancer?

The answer is regular exercise. Hundreds of studies conducted over the past 50 years demonstrate that exercise helps you feel better and live longer.

We have just explored food and nutrition. Good, healthy food will give you the energy required to do exercise and perform physical activities easily and safely.

Why should we exercise?
What is exercise?
How do people feel when they hear this word, "exercise"?

One category of people frown or make long faces when they hear this word. They will quickly come up with excuses not to discuss the topic further. Some will tell you straight up that they don't need it and they don't feel it's important. Some will say that they walk to work, or they have several household chores or they have to walk from the station to their office, and that's good enough exercise for them.

Another category will try and make attempts to get some exercise in their lives. They will start off all motivated and then lose steam along the way. They have to be reminded, prodded on and coached all the time, to go out and exercise.

Another category cannot go a day without doing some exercise. If they don't exercise, they feel irritable through the day, they experience low energy levels and they seem somewhat lethargic and depressed. Rain or sunshine, they will do their bit for the day.

Which category do you fall in? What's the big deal about exercise anyway?

To understand all of that, we must first understand the meaning of the term "exercise". Many people immediately link the word to a graphical image of sweaty bodies in the gym, slugging heavy weights, running on machines or cycling and doing hundreds of crunches.

Let's go with the Wikipedia definition before we delve into this topic.

Physical exercise:
Physical exercise is any bodily activity that enhances or maintains physical fitness and overall health or wellness. It is performed for various reasons. These include strengthening muscles and the cardiovascular system, honing athletic skills, weight loss or maintenance and for enjoyment.

Exercises are generally grouped into three types depending on the overall effect they have on the human body:

- ➔ Flexibility exercises, such as stretching, improves the range of motion of Muscles and joints

- ➔ Aerobic exercises, such as cycling, swimming, walking, skipping rope, rowing, running, hiking or playing tennis, focus on increasing cardiovascular endurance

- ➔ Anaerobic exercises, such as weight training, functional training or sprinting, increase short-term muscle strength

By making your goal "FITNESS", you will automatically incorporate exercise in it. This is because exercise is required to improve your:

- ➔ Cardiovascular health
- ➔ Flexibility
- ➔ Strength
- ➔ Stamina
- ➔ Lung capacity
- ➔ Agility and balance
- ➔ Speed
- ➔ Power
- ➔ Accuracy and coordination

Seems like a long list, but guess what? Mostly any from of exercise that you choose will help you develop all of the above, though there will be some sports and exercises that focus more on a couple of them, depending on the usage and requirement of that part.

Physical exercise is important for maintaining physical fitness and can contribute positively to maintaining a healthy weight, building and maintaining healthy bone density, muscle strength, and joint mobility, promoting physiological well-being, reducing surgical risks, and strengthening the immune system.

Exercise also reduces the levels of cortisol. Cortisol is a stress hormone that builds fat in the abdominal region, making weight loss difficult. Cortisol causes many health problems, both physical and mental.

Frequent and regular aerobic exercise has been shown to help prevent or treat serious and life-threatening chronic conditions such as high blood pressure, obesity, heart disease, Type 2 diabetes, insomnia, and depression.

There are several benefits of exercise:

Exercise makes your heart stronger

In the early caveman days, there were no automobiles, so people walked, the wells did not have pumps, so people pulled, no supermarkets to shop for food, so people hunted game and climbed trees. They had more active lives than us. In today's world people lead sedentary lives, all thanks to technology. We have more comfortable lives but at the cost of physical activity. The wide array of packaged foods and sweets and sugars don't make it easier on our bodies. So we gain weight and our heart has to work faster and harder to ensure blood circulation. It works in overdrive when it has to pump blood forcefully through arteries that are clogged with fat caused by unhealthy foods. But when we exercise, our actions make the heart work harder and the heart is a muscle. With exercise its walls get stonger and thicker. Blood keeps flowing faster through the arteries, keeping them clean and healthy. This is why we need exercise, all the more because our lives have become sedentary. Without the heart we cannot live, so we must exercise to keep it healthy and clean. Many times I am asked about red meat. Why is red meat bad. The caveman's staple diet was meat. Meat is high in saturated fat, but the cavemen had different lifestyles. They burnt as much of calories as they ate, in absence of technology and amenities. The quality of meat was so much more organic and healthier than what we have today.

Blood Circulation

Blood carries oxygen and nutrients to all the parts of our body. Nutrients are required for our health and growth. When you exercise, your heart rate increases and so does your blood circulation, which means quicker circulation of oxygen and nutrients as well. Due to gravity, blood may not circulate too well in the upper parts of our body. Ever noticed how your face turns red or pink after exercise? That's the blood flowing in the capillaries beneath your skin. Exercise caused that increased circulation. Ever noticed how you feel a little dizzy when you bend over and stand up straight after a bit? That's the blood and oxygen rushing to your head, which otherwise may not happen effectively with normal circulation. Exercise ensures efficient delivery of nutrients and oxygen through increased blood circulation in our body.

Increased metabolism and energy

We discussed what metabolism was all about in the Food chapter. Exercise enhances your metabolism. In turn, you have great energy levels. That's why exercise can be so addictive for some people. The energy they experience after exercise is like a high, and they want more of it. When we exercise, we break down muscle, and to repair itself, the body burns calories, and this is what keeps your body metabolism high.

To maintain your body tone and lean mass requires energy, and your body constantly burns calories to provide this energy, resulting in a great metabolism. Exercise increases blood circulation which, in turn, increases the amount of oxygen circulating through your body resulting into great energy levels and a feeling of freshness.

Increased self-esteem
Gaining control of your body size and weight through fitness is an amazing way to increase self-esteem. You look better and are more confident which empowers you in everything you do. You will find that the self-discipline required and learned through regular exercise spills over into other areas of your life and you will be better able to make other necessary and desirable changes.

Mental health
Did you know that the latest research shows that exercise helps keep the brain sharp during old age? Anything that involves mental activity (focus and concentration) is improved. You also stand a much better chance of avoiding such diseases as Alzheimer's and senility.

Maintain healthy weight
Most diseases today are weight related. Our bodies are designed to carry our ideal weight. Anything over our ideal weight puts stress on the body, on our bones, and our internal organs especially our heart. Extra fat disturbs the normal function of our body. Most doctors and nutritionists will confidently state that if you reduce your belly fat and get your weight in place, a lot of our medical conditions will disappear our medication dosages will slowly decrease and finally stop. Exercise will help us maintain a healthy weight and burn off excess fat.

Increases strength and stamina
Exercise will develop our stamina and endurance. It will give us the strength to go easily through a day of chores and tasks without feeling drained out and famished. Exercise strengthens our bones and develops our muscles so we can go through our everyday lives easily and without causing injury to our bodies.

Reduces depression
The production of Endorphins (Feel good hormones) is increased through exercise. Nothing improves mood and suppresses depression better than those endorphins. That's why exercise can get addictive.

Decreased stress levels
The worries and stresses of everyday living (commuting, work demands, conflicts, etc.) can stick with you long after the workday is done. Exercise right after work is the perfect natural therapy that can change your mood. You'll sleep better too!

Health of your joints

Regular exercise will keep your limbs and joints supple and healthy. As you age, you will find that physical activity is restricted amongst those who do not exercise. Our joints are like the hinges on a door. They need to be oiled regularly in order to work well. In between our joints there is a fluid that allows for this lubrication.

Exercise keeps this lubricant in circulation and prevents joint related diseases like Arthritis. Exercise to keep your bones, joints and limbs strong.

Exercise keeps you young and adds years to your life. Stonger the heart, the longer you live. Cells need oxygen to grow and replicate, proper blood circulation will allow for this. New cells means faster recovery from illness and younger looking skin, stronger nails and rich hair growth.

Lean mass versus Fat

The human body is composed of lean mass (muscle) , fat and water. The more lean mass you develop, the less fat you have, and your metabolism gets stronger. Your body moves into 'auto-burn' mode when your lean mass percentage is higher. To develop lean mass, you eat the right foods and you do strength training exercises coupled with aerobics.

There are several other benefits of exercise. That's why it's so important that we make every effort possible to get exercise into our daily schedules.

- ➔ Enhances quality of sleep
- ➔ Adds a sparkle and radiance to complexion
- ➔ Improves body shape
- ➔ Tones and firms muscles
- ➔ Provides more muscular definition
- ➔ Increases lean muscle tissue in the body
- ➔ Improves appetite for healthy foods
- ➔ Alleviates menstrual cramps
- ➔ Improves posture
- ➔ Eases and possibly eliminates back problems and pain
- ➔ Makes the body use calories more efficiently
- ➔ Lowers resting heart rate
- ➔ Increases muscle size through an increase in muscle fibers
- ➔ Improves body composition
- ➔ Increases body density
- ➔ Decreases fat tissue more easily
- ➔ Improves athletic performance
- ➔ Enriches sexuality
- ➔ Improves liver functioning
- ➔ Makes calcium transport in the heart and body more efficient

Interesting isn't it? There is so much you can gain by just doing exercise, and it gets simpler too. I need to keep reminding you that it's all about keeping it simple and making balanced choices. Before we go any further, let's discuss the dreaded word "FAT".

Why do people become fat?
Is fat a bad thing?
What can we do to reduce the fat in our body?

People become fat when they eat more than what their bodies require. Now it is practically impossible and an arduous process to measure and control exactly how many calories we need. That's why we need to exercise, to burn the extra calories that our body does not need.

It's as simple as that. You exercise to burn excess calories, so they do not get stored as fat. Picture this. Your body has 25 billion to 40 billion fat cells. Imagine each of them as a collapsible, fine walled container. If you eat calories that you don't need, that is your body does not break them down into energy, then these calories go into these little containers (cells), and get stored as fat. So over the weeks, months and years, these billions of cells fill up and have a profound effect on your body weight and health. Your body has almost unlimited capacity to store fat. It gets really bad when you find your body beginning to store fat around your abdomen.

Even if you are moderately overweight, you are carrying a constant burden on your back and legs. Eventually this can aggravate conditions like degenerative arthritis (osteoarthritis). Being overweight also puts you at a higher risk for complications following surgery, because wounds don't heal as well or as fast and infection is more common. In addition, obesity also has direct links to diseases that can shorten your life. It increases your resistance to insulin and is the leading cause of type 2 diabetes. Your liver produces more triglycerides and less HDL (good cholesterol), you become vulnerable to cardiovascular disease, including stroke and high blood pressure. You have an increased risk of developing breast, prostrate, colon and uterus cancer, gallstones and respiratory problems such as sleep apnea increases.

Yes, being fat is bad. The good part is, it's simple to keep it off. If you are fat, you just need to start doing simple things, making simple lifestyle changes and you go from fat to healthy.

People see the task of reducing fat as a hard and difficult journey and many choose to live with the consequences. It's as simple as this. If you are poor, you will work hard to get rich. Apply the same logic. If you are overweight, you must work to get fit.

She prefers that her name is not mentioned. She lives in Spain, and we met in India a year and a half ago. She had a great job and a lovely family. After checking her medical reports, it was clear that she needed to lose weight quickly. That, in turn, would bring down her blood pressure and improve her sleep apnea condition. She was at the borderline for diabetes and her bad cholesterol levels surely had to come down. The good thing, I explained to her was that "If you just reduce your fat percentage, all of these ailments will slowly disappear." She was strong on the point that she did not want to go to gym or join any weight loss camp, and I was strong about the point that fat pills and burners were out of the question. So we finally agreed upon a natural food plan built to power her metabolism, filled with vitamin and nutrient rich foods, coupled with 6 days of 45 minutes brisk walks and daily stretching. The target was 800 grams of weight loss a week. By week 3 she was losing 1.3kgs a week, with minor changes in her food plan and the same exercise schedule.

The point of the above story is that weight loss is simple. We tend to complicate simple things like this. I have a client who joined one of Mumbai's exclusive gyms. The annual fee was huge. The services included were valet parking, massages, personal trainers, welcome drinks, hot towels, ipod enabled machines, altitude training zones, consultancy with nutritionists, weight loss electronic belts and I forget the other services, which were numerous. Out of 30 days in that month, during our meet I learnt that he had gone to the gym 9 times that month. Too much traffic, driver on leave, massage appointment cancelled, were some of the main reasons for his absence from the gym. So much for a huge annual fee.

Exercise is a simple concept. Keep it simple. Choose something that works for you, something that you can fit into your hectic day, something you can fit in if you have to travel. Travel plans should not be the reason to cancel your exercise plan or miss out on a workout.

Choose your goal. If your goal is fat loss, your choice of exercise would be different. If your goal is muscle and body sculpture, the exercise you choose would be different. It is so important to understand your goal and then choose an exercise plan that will help you achieve that goal and it should be something you enjoy. Let's have a look at various types of exercises and sports that you can choose from.

Aerobic Exercises:
A successful aerobic exercise program involves frequent physical activity that is rhythmic, repetitive, challenges the circulatory system, and uses large muscles. The exercise program must significantly increase the blood flow to the muscles for an extended period of time, promoting cardiovascular fitness. Such exercises are called isotonic, dynamic, or aerobic. If you want to have a healthy heart, you need to perform aerobic exercise.

You should choose aerobic exercises to burn fat as well. Your body breaks down excess calories and fat in your body to provide energy to sustain your aerobic workout. You should also choose aerobic exercises to improve your stamina, endurance and your game, if you play any sport. Examples of aerobic exercises are:

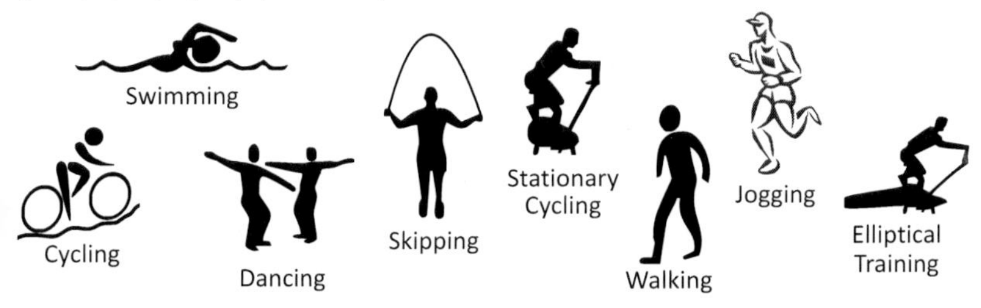

Flexibility Exercises
Flexibility is an important component of a well-rounded fitness program. Most individuals tend to become tight and stiff with age. It is important to maintain normal flexibility for several reasons. Good flexibility reduces the probability that you will suffer from back pain and other postural types of pain syndromes. Normal flexibility also allows you to attain normal movement patterns in all activities and requires you to expend less energy as you go through your daily activities.

Yoga is a great flexibility exercise. All stretching exercises get categorized under flexibility training. Combining aerobics with flexibility training reaps tons of benefits for the body. Besides keeping your muscles, limbs and joints supple, your body even burns calories when you stretch. Flexibility leads to body tone.

Body tone is nothing but the energy burned by your body to hold its muscles in place. A toned body is firm and supple, whereas an un-toned body is loose and saggy.

Flexibility training will give you that toned and supple look.

Strength Training

Many people don't realize the numerous benefits of a sound strength-training program: increase in muscle size (if desired) and tone; increased muscle, tendon, bone, and ligament strength; increased physical performance and appearance; improved metabolic efficiency; and decreased risk of injury.

You would require a home gym or a commercial gym to train for strength. This training involves weights as resistance or special machines that can provide resistance through sheer weight or hydraulics. Supervision is suggested if you are a beginner, because incorrect form can lead to serious injuries. A good strength-training plan includes different exercises for different body parts. Your fitness consultant will help you compile a plan based on your goal and your current strength. It is always suggested that you go through a fitness test before beginning a program, to evaluate your body stats. Based on the results, an appropriate plan can be drawn up for you.

Once you know your goal, choose the exercise that best suits you and your needs.

Exercise equipment:

There are several kinds of exercise equipment available across the globe, each piece promising different results. Ab rollers, toners, bull workers, weight machines, medicine balls and so on. I am reminding you again, keep it simple. If you understood the types of exercise as discussed above, you will find that all these fancy machines are not required. In most cases using your own body weight, carefully designed exercises and the right form are sufficient to produce the desired results if the goal is general fitness and weight-loss. A good trainer will help you master the technique and watch out for your form.

Injury:

The purpose of exercise is not to injure yourself, yet a staggering number of people injure themselves while working out. Injuries during exercise are caused due to:

- → **Poor form:** Incorrect technique and posture will lead to muscle pulls and sprains. It can result in serious back injury and injury to the joints and muscles.

➔ **Overdoing it:** Everyone's body is built differently. Know when to stop. Listen to your body and don't over exercise. It puts undue stress on your muscles and limbs and will lead to fatigue and injury.

➔ **Poor nutrition:** You need the right nutrition plan to support your exercise schedule. Poor nutrition can lead to calcium and vitamin deficiencies, which, in turn, can lead to injury. If you are using sports supplements, you must consult a sports nutritionist to understand which product and how much of it is okay for you.

➔ **Supervision:** Depending on your level of fitness and type of exercise you choose, it is important to engage the help of a trainer who will watch your form and prevent you from getting injured.

As you exercise more regularly your body will get stronger and you will be able to exceed your previous day's target. That's progress, but don't overdo it at the cost of safety. Avoid sustaining injury.

That's all you need to know about the basics of exercise. As you can see, exercise and nutrition go hand in hand. You may have the best food plan, but without exercise, you will not be able to achieve fitness levels and vice versa.

Try and make exercise fun. Long walks or jogs with loved ones are a great way to exercise. My clients in Antwerp, Belgium, enjoy 1.5 hour-long walks in the beautiful green parks that the city boasts of. What a great way to exercise and breathe in fresh air.

Choose something that works with you and partner up with a buddy. It's motivating and you get your work out done.

Exercising your options

So how much exercise do you need?

Just enough to meet your goals. Make health your priority, and remember to get a check-up before you start a big new exercise push. Choose the activities that best fit your schedule, your budget, your abilities, and your taste. Construct a balanced program by adding weight training, stretching, and exercises for balance that you need. Start slowly, build up gradually, and—above all—stick with it.

SLEEP AND REST:

The third element of fitness is sleep and rest. Why must humans sleep? How does it contribute towards a fitter you?

Sleep is defined as a state of unconsciousness from which a person can be aroused. Sleep is essential for the normal, healthy functioning of the human body. It is a complicated physiological phenomenon that scientists do not fully understand.

Sleep affects our physical and mental health, and is essential for the normal functioning of all the systems of our body, including the immune system. The effect of sleep on the immune system affects one's ability to fight disease and endure sickness. Animal studies have shown that sleep is necessary for survival. The normal life span of rats is 2-3 years. However, rats deprived of sleep live for only about 3 weeks. They also develop abnormally low body temperatures and sores on their tails and paws. The sores probably develop because of impairment of the rats' immune systems. In humans, it has been demonstrated that the metabolic activity of the brain decreases significantly after 24 hours of sustained wakefulness. Sleep deprivation results in a decrease in body temperature, a decrease in immune system function as measured by white blood cell count (the soldiers of the body), and a decrease in the release of growth hormone. Sleep deprivation can also cause increased heart rate variability.

For our nervous system to work properly, sleep is needed. Sleep deprivation makes a person drowsy and unable to concentrate the next day. It also leads to impairment of memory and physical performance and reduced ability to carry out mathematical calculations. If sleep deprivation continues, hallucinations and mood swings may develop.

Release of growth hormone in children and young adults takes place during deep sleep. Most cells of the body show increased production and reduced breakdown of proteins during deep sleep. Sleep helps humans maintain optimal emotional and social functioning while we are awake by giving rest during sleep to the parts of the brain that control emotions and social interactions.

For adults, sleep of 8-8.4 hours is considered fully restorative. In some cultures, total sleep is often divided into an overnight sleep period of 6-7 hours and a nap of 1-2 hours.

Some people may need as little as 5 hours or as much as 10 hours of sleep every day. The period of time a person sleeps depends also on the fact whether he or she has been deprived of sleep in previous days. Sleeping too little creates a "sleep debt." This debt needs to be adjusted by sleeping for longer periods over the next few days. People who sleep less have an impairment of judgment and reaction time.

Sleep rhythms can be affected to a certain degree by almost any kind of external stimulus, for example, the beeping of the alarm clock or the timing of meals. When we cross time zones, our circadian rhythms get disrupted leading to jet lag. It usually takes several days for our body rhythms to adjust to the new time.

Symptoms similar to those seen in people with jet lag are common in people who work during nights or work in shifts. Because these people's wake time conflicts with powerful sleep-regulating cues like sunlight, they often become uncontrollably drowsy during work or may have difficulty falling asleep during their off time. Their biological clock wants to do one thing, while they are doing something entirely different. People working in shifts have an increased risk of heart, gastrointestinal, emotional, and mental problems. All these problems may be related to the disruption of the sleep rhythm.

According to the National Sleep Foundation, "If you have trouble keeping your eyes focused, if you can't stop yawning, or if you can't remember driving the last few miles, you are probably too drowsy to drive safely." It is important to know that caffeine and other stimulants cannot overcome the effects of severe sleep deprivation. Therefore, if you find yourself driving in a sleep-deprived state, it is imperative that you find a safe place to stop and catch up on your sleep before continuing safely on your way.

Obesity and Sleep:
Believe it or not, the two are linked. Studies have proven that those who sleep for lesser hours or have irregular sleep patterns, struggle to maintain a healthy weight. In fact when you sleep less, your metabolism falls, and in turn, your body struggles to burn calories through the day. Lack of sleep leads to hormone imbalance and, in turn, can have a dramatic effect on weight loss or fat gain. Our body's are designed to perform certain functions during our sleep, so if you cut out on your sleep, you cut into a natural process. The body's ability to process glucose (sugar) also decreases with fewer hours of sleep. Sleep experts say there are a number of things you can do to lose weight and improve your sleep:

- ➔ Make healthy choices for your meals. Avoid fast foods. Eat more fish, fruits and vegetables; avoid foods high in carbohydrates or fats.

- ➔ Start getting consistent exercise, which will improve the quality of your sleep. Most experts, however, advise us to avoid exercising less than 3 hours before bedtime, because exercise is alerting and can make it harder to fall asleep.

- ➔ Examine your sleep schedule. Are you getting at least 7 hours of sleep each night? Do you wake up feeling refreshed or lethargic? Do you wake up frequently during the night? Are you underweight, overweight, or just right?

Workouts and Sleep:
A productive workout is just not measured on how many minutes or hours you exercised. It goes further. What are the results of your workout? Your body burns calories even when you sleep.

When you exercise your muscles get broken down (not literally) and they get repaired, which means that they develop in size or strength when your body is at rest. So if you have less sleep or rest, your muscles don't recover completely and there are chances that you may get injured during your next workout.

Several people I know pump iron or run every single day of the week, and these people struggle to achieve their fitness goal and end up getting frustrated, or trying even harder. The key is rest. Let your body and muscles recover and you will find your next workout all the more productive. A great workout will promote a good night's sleep. Sometimes you will find that your body requires more sleep. It usually depends on the amount of physical activity you had during the day and also the amount of mental stress.

Stress:
The less sleep you have, the more susceptible is your body and mind to stress. Less sleep does not allow for the complete recovery of your brain cells, and this can result in irritability, emotional instability, depression the next day or over the course of the week. In several sessions with clients, when they say they had a rough day or they were depressed or irritable, I ask them to reflect on the previous night's sleep or sleep pattern during that week, and in almost all cases, the client had slept irregularly and for less than 5 hours. If you wake up fresh you've had enough sleep. If you wake up tired and lethargic and still craving to sleep a little more, your body is asking you for more sleep. It needs rest.

Working Shifts:
A shift worker is anyone who follows a work schedule that is outside of the typical '9 to 5' business day. From a competitive standpoint, shift work is an excellent way to increase production and customer service without major increases in infrastructure. However, while shift work does create potential productivity advantages, it also has many inherent risks. Some of the most serious and persistent problems shift workers face are frequent sleep disturbance and associated excessive sleepiness. Sleepiness/fatigue in the work place can lead to poor concentration, absenteeism, accidents, errors, injuries, and fatalities. The issue becomes more alarming when you consider that shift workers are often employed in the most dangerous of jobs, such as firefighting, emergency medical services, law enforcement and security. Managers and policy makers who are responsible for writing and enforcing rules regarding employee work hours must address the specific issues of a 24-hour work force in order to succeed and benefit from such a labor force. Although addressing these issues may require some investment up front for training and other measures, the bottom line is that improved sleep in workers may lead to improved productivity.

In fact, to ignore the needs of the shift worker is reckless and irresponsible when you consider that billions of dollars in yearly costs, thousands of deaths, and some of the most notorious of modern catastrophes such as the failure of the Space Shuttle Columbia and the crash of the Exxon Valdez have been attributed to human fatigue. According to the International Classifications of Sleep Disorders, shift workers are at increased risk for a variety of chronic illnesses such as cardiovascular and gastrointestinal diseases. Whether this is related to the fact that shift workers are awake and active during the night hours or because they tend to get fewer hours of sleep overall than traditional workers is not known. Also, shift workers often miss out on important family and social events due to their work schedules. Most managers recognize that understanding and addressing these issues improves employee morale, performance, safety and health, and can dramatically improve the bottom line of the company.

People who work in the transportation industry face some of the most serious challenges. They battle fatigue because of their irregular sleep schedules and endure long tedious hours at the controls or behind the wheel. In fact, research suggests that driver fatigue behind the wheel caused by sleep deprivation is one of the leading safety hazards in the transportation industry.

The main complaint for people with shift work sleep disorder is excessive sleepiness. Other symptoms include:

- ➔ Insomnia
- ➔ Disrupted sleep schedules
- ➔ Reduced performance
- ➔ Difficulties with personal relationships
- ➔ Irritability/depressed mood

If you are a shift worker and have difficulty sleeping during the day, chances are you also have difficulty staying awake at work. Also, the more sleepy/fatigued you are, the more likely you are to experience a "microsleep," an involuntary bout of sleep brought on by sleep deprivation that lasts for a few seconds.

Here are some tips for staying alert on the job:

- ➔ Avoid long commutes and extended hours.
- ➔ Take short nap breaks throughout the shift.
- ➔ Work with others to help keep you alert.
- ➔ Try to be active during breaks (e.g., take a walk, shoot hoops in the parking lot, or even exercise).

- Drink a caffeinated beverage (coffee, tea, colas) to help maintain alertness during the shift.

- Don't leave the most tedious or boring tasks to the end of your shift when you are apt to feel the drowsiest. Night shift workers are most sleepy around 4-5 a.m.

- Exchange ideas with your colleagues on ways to cope with the problems of shift work. Set up a support group at work so that you can discuss these issues and learn from each other.

Here are some tips for sleeping during the day:

- Wear dark glasses to block out the sunlight on your way home.
- Keep to the same bedtime and wake time schedule, even on weekends.
- Eliminate noise and light from your sleep environment (use eye masks and ear plugs).
- Avoid caffeinated beverages and foods close to bedtime.
- Avoid alcohol; although it may seem to improve sleep initially, tolerance develops quickly and it will soon disturb sleep.

Sleep and School Children:

Children aged five to 12 need 10-11 hours of sleep. At the same time, there is an increasing demand on their time from school (e.g., homework), sports and other extracurricular and social activities. In addition, school-aged children become more interested in TV, computers, the media and Internet as well as caffeine products – all of which can lead to difficulty falling asleep, nightmares and disruptions to their sleep. In particular, watching TV close to bedtime has been associated with bedtime resistance, difficulty falling asleep, anxiety around sleep and sleeping fewer hours.

Sleep problems and disorders are prevalent at this age. Poor or inadequate sleep can lead to mood swings, behavioral problems such as hyperactivity and cognitive problems that impact on their ability to learn in school.

Sleep Tips for School-aged Children

- Teach school-aged children about healthy sleep habits.
- Continue to emphasize the need for regular and consistent sleep schedule and bedtime routine.
- Make the child's bedroom conducive to sleep - dark, cool and quiet.
- Keep TV and computers out of the bedroom.
- Avoid caffeine.

Caffeine and Sleep:
Caffeine has been called the most popular drug in the world.All over the world people consume caffeine on a daily basis in coffee, tea, cocoa, chocolate, some soft drinks, and some drugs.

Because caffeine is a stimulant, most people use it after waking up in the morning or to remain alert during the day. While it is important to note that caffeine cannot replace sleep, it can temporarily make us feel more alert by blocking sleep-inducing chemicals in the brain and increasing adrenaline production.

There is no nutritional need for caffeine in the diet. Moderate caffeine intake, however, is not associated with any recognized health risk.

Caffeine enters the bloodstream through the stomach and small intestine and can have a stimulating effect as soon as 15 minutes after it is consumed. Once in the body, caffeine will persist for several hours: it takes about 6 hours for one half of the caffeine to be eliminated. There are numerous studies to support the idea that caffeine causes physical dependence. If you suspect that you or someone you know is dependent on caffeine, the best test is to eliminate it and look for signs of withdrawal, such as headache, fatigue and muscle pain.

Although caffeine is safe to consume in moderation, it is not recommended for children. It may negatively affect a child's nutrition by replacing nutrient-dense foods such as milk. A child may also eat less because caffeine acts as an appetite suppressant. Caffeine can be safely eliminated from a child's diet since there is no nutritional requirement for it.

Caffeine is a stimulant. In moderate doses, it can:
➔ Increase alertness
➔ Reduce fine motor coordination
➔ Cause insomnia
➔ Cause headaches, nervousness and dizziness

It has also been known to result in:
➔ Anxiety
➔ Irritability
➔ Rapid heartbeat
➔ Excessive urination
➔ Sleep disturbance
➔ A "caffeine crash" once the effects wear off

If the conditions listed above occur, discontinue the use of caffeine. These effects are more likely to occur if caffeine is consumed in large doses. Children and women who are nursing or pregnant should avoid caffeine. People who are taking any prescription medication should talk to their doctors before consuming caffeine.

Knowing the caffeine content of your food and drinks can help you keep caffeine intake at a healthy level so you can still reap the benefits of a good night's sleep.

In order to sleep better at night and reduce daytime sleepiness, try practicing the following sleep tips:

- ➔ Maintain a regular bed and wake time schedule including weekends
- ➔ Establish a regular, relaxing bedtime routine such as taking a bath or listening to music
- ➔ Create a sleep-conducive environment that is dark, quiet, comfortable and cool
- ➔ Sleep on a comfortable mattress and pillows
- ➔ Use your bedroom only for sleep and sex
- ➔ Finish eating at least 2-3 hours before your regular bedtime
- ➔ Exercise regularly but avoid it a few hours before bedtime
- ➔ Avoid caffeine (e.g. coffee, tea, soft drinks, chocolate) close to bedtime
- ➔ Don't smoke - not only is it a major health risk, it can lead to poor sleep
- ➔ Avoid alcohol close to bedtime; it can lead to disrupted sleep later in the night

Sleep therapists today suggest that you listen to your body. It's the best indicator for how much sleep you require, though you must draw the line between sleeping out of laziness, and requirement. These two elements should not be confused. The same way some people eat when they are bored or depressed, some people sleep.

Aim for deep and undisturbed sleep. 7 hours of irregular sleep may not be the best solution.

Goals:

As you move into the next section of this book, you will understand why I encourage you to set your fitness goals and make entries on a daily basis.

It's really very simple. Some people have financial goals. The goal is a 'target sum of money or wealth' that they want to achieve, and most people who have goals, have usually thought of a way or means to achieve it.

Most people are surprised to know that the reason they are not getting what they want in life is because their major goals are too small and too vague, and therefore have no power. Your major goal will not be reached if it fails to excite your imagination.

Set a power goal - a power goal is a dream that drives you. People who create power goal are living on purpose. It's not what a goal is, that matters. It's what a goal does to you.

Soccer would be a meaningless game if there were no goal posts. You would have the players running all over the field not knowing where to shoot the ball.

Some people feel goals are pressurizing and put constraints on their freedom. They just want to be happy and relaxed. Well that's a goal too, being happy and relaxed. There would be certain things that one would do or have to do in order to be happy and relaxed.

I encourage each of you to think about your fitness goal. It could be anything ranging from weight-loss to training for a marathon, to just general fitness to lead a happy and healthy life.But write this goal down and write down how you plan to achieve it. Once you have your goal clearly thought of and on paper, then you may consult friends or professionals or do research on the best ways to achieve them.

The next section of the journal has templates to help you plan and enter your goals and ways to achieve them. The success of reaching any goal is tracking, recording and writing down everything. It helps you stay aware of how close you are to your goal, and what changes have to be made if any.

How to shape your goal ? A simple tip.
Keep all goals **'SMART'**
Let's use an example to illustrate this better. Let's assume you want to run the marathon. How do we make this a 'SMART' goal?

S: Specific
Define how many miles you plan to finish on the big day and in how much time?

M: Measurable
By recording the miles you wish to finish and the time in which you want to do it, you have now made your goal 'measurable'.

A: Achievable
All goals should be achievable. Set the distance that you think you can achieve.

R: Realistic

The goal should be able to materialize. For example, if you are recovering from a knee injury or an operation, is your goal realistic?

T: Time bound

All goals should be time bound for them to be realized. For example, you need to be running 10 kilometers by the third week of training. Your average pace needs to increase from 'X' to 'Y' by the 4th week.

Every time you make a goal, run it through the 'SMART' checker.
Remember, a goal without an action plan written, is a dream.
Write down your goals, record your daily entries and watch your life change.
Keep it simple, shape your goal and shape up.

In the box below, think and then write down your goal, your vision and your dream

Positive Thinking and Attitude

It's been said that positive thinking can boost your attitude and motivation, and help you have a better life.

Many people report that their lives have been changed just by altering their thought patterns. When you learn the principles and apply them in your own life, you will see miracles start to happen.

It's defined as a conscious effort to focus your thoughts upward. Gradually you will develop a mind-set of thinking in this way, leading to a lifetime of happiness and joy. This way of thinking has helped countless people live happier lives.

Studies show that there is a happiness-health connection, and thinking positively can actually improve your health. People who are upbeat, positive thinkers have fewer colds and other health problems than people who are down.

Change your Thoughts

You can read all the books, watch all the videos or DVDs in the world on how to be happy, but true happiness will be elusive until you learn to change your thoughts.

Here are a few guidelines for harnessing this incredible power:

1. Decide to be Happy.

It sounds simple, and indeed it is. Tell yourself that no matter what happens, you will have joy in your heart. You and you alone are in control of your emotions. Decide right now to be happy.

2. Only think Positive Thoughts.

Whenever you find your mind wandering to something negative, quickly snap it back to the positive.

3. Visualize your Future.

Whatever it is that you would like to be or have, close your eyes and picture it in your mind. Then go one step further and actually try to feel what it would be like to be in that place. Smell the scents, hear the sounds, feel the emotions of joy that you will have.

4. Begin Using Affirmations.

Affirmations are statements you make aloud which reinforce your goals to your sub-conscious. There is ample evidence that these affirmations can have a tremendous impact on your life.

Here are some examples of affirmations. I encourage you to write down your own and practice them while driving, when you wake up, before you sleep, in the bathroom, just about anywhere. The more you practice them, your mind begins to get programmed, and your mind is connected to billions of cells which will bring about positive transformation.

You can start today to change your thoughts to have a healthier, happier life!

- I am perfectly healthy in body, mind and spirit.
- I am well, I am whole, and I am strong and healthy.
- I never get sick.
- I am healthy, happy and radiant.
- I radiate good health.
- My body is a safe and pleasurable place for me to be.
- My sleep is relaxed and refreshing.
- I have all the energy I need to accomplish my goals.
- My body is healed, restored and filled with energy.
- I have abundant energy, vitality and well-being.
- I am healthy in all aspects of my being.
- I am always able to maintain my ideal weight.
- I am filled with energy to do all the daily activities in my life.
- My mind is at peace.
- Every day, in every way, I am becoming better and better.
- I am healthy and happy.
- I love and care for my body and it cares for me

When you make these statements, joyfully envision your body in perfect health. Close your eyes and picture a healthy, vibrant new you. Speaking these out loud rather than just thinking about them is also important.

If you make this a daily practice, in a short time you may see significant improvements in your body, your health and your life.

5. Practice Forgiveness.
Holding on to grudges can create all sorts of physical ailments. Releasing the negative thoughts is liberating. There's a secret to forgiveness - it's a gift you give to yourself.

6. Don't Think about the Past.
Focus on the future and on what you would like to accomplish. Anything is possible if you set your mind to it and never give up.

7. Believe it will Happen.
This is the most important point to remember. Any doubt is negative energy and should not be allowed to enter your mind.

There are many good books available for further reading. One of the best books I've ever read on this topic is the classic 'The Power of Positive Thinking'. It has tons of inspiration and I highly recommend it.

Remember...
If you change your thoughts, you can change your life.

Become a Person of Action:
And again I repeat, a goal without an action plan is a dream, and an action plan without action is just a plan.

I would like to share an excerpt from Napolean Hill's 'Law of Success'. "No matter how fantastic your plans maybe, they will be useless if they are not expressed in action. To dream and to see visions of the person you would like to be, you should transform your dreams and visions into reality and action.

Your body is made up of billions of tiny cells that are highly sensitive and connected to your mind. If your mind is lethargic, your body will become lazy and inactive also. If you doubt this, the next time you feel lazy think about an activity that you are fond of and notice how quickly the cells of your body will respond on to your enthusiasm and your lazy feeling will disappear. The cells of the body respond to your state of mind in exactly the same manner that the people in the city will respond to the mass psychology that dominates the city. An active and dynamic mind keeps the cells of your body in a constant state of activity.

Thinking can be as valuable to the health as your walk. You cannot be a person of action if you overeat and under exercise, neither can you be a person of action if you run to the pill bottle every time you have or imagine you have an ache or a pain.

I have enthusiasm, endurance and action because I eat the simple food that contains the body building elements that I require.

There is another enemy you must conquer to become a person of action. That is the Worry habit. Worry, envy, jealousy, hatred, doubt and fear are all states of mind that are fatal to action. These negatives states of mind destroy the most essential factor in the achievement of success, the desire to achieve. You cannot achieve when you are in a negative state of mind." (Napolean Hill)

Take full possession and responsibility for your mind and the thoughts you think, because thoughts become actions and actions become who we are.

The only thing that you have complete control over, is your mental attitude.

You hear people telling you that "it's all in the mind" and guess what, it is.

If you have a burning desire to get fit, you will.

If you have a burning desire to run the marathon, you will.

If you have a burning desire to wear a bikini on your next vacation, you will.

If you have a burning desire to fit into a dress or pair of jeans, you will.

If you have a burning desire to stay free of medication and achieve health through food, exercise and sleep, you will.

If you have a burning desire to be happy, healthy and age gracefully, you will.

Have a burning desire to be able to do 15 or 20 years down the line all that you do today.

No matter what mutual funds, stocks or investments you make, they hold no value if you have not invested in your health.

Now is time you Shape up!

"The secret of getting ahead is getting started." - Mark Twain

60 Days
Success Journey
Commit to get fit,
It’s your life,
SHAPE IT

Shape Your Goals
Sharing Statistics

Measurements		**Current**	**8 Week goal**
Height: _____ Feet _____ Inches			
Weight - Pounds/Kg	:	______	______
Body Fat %	:	______	______
Blood pressure	:	______	______
Resting heart rate	:	______	______

Exercise

Total workout time (per day)	:	______	______
Total no. of workout days in a week	:	______	______

Sleep

Hours per night	:	______	______

Medical History : ____________________________________

____

____

Current Medication : ____________________________________

____

____

To reach my goals I plan to : ____________________________________

____

____

“REGENERATED”

Weekly Goals ____________________ ____________________

Plan Your Week

	Mon	Tue	Wed	Thur	Fri	Sat	Sun
xercise							
wim							
Valk							
un							
lliptical							
ycle							
Veights							
orts							
ga							
ther:							
est day							
od							
t outs							
der in							
etox							
eligious fast							
eep							
Hours							
Hours							
7 Hours							
assage							

These are your goals for the week. Strive to achieve them.
"A goal without an action plan, is a dream"

Date: | Week: # | Day: # | Day of week:

No. of hours sleep (previous night)

Food Notes

Upon waking

Time:

Breakfast

Time:

Snack 1

Time:

Lunch

Time:

Snack 2

Time:

Snack 3

Time:

Dinner

Time:

Before Sleep

Time:

Water ☐ ☐ ☐ ☐ ☐ ☐ ☐ ☐ ☐
☐ ☐ ☐ ☐ ☐ ☐ ☐ ☐ ☐

Vitamins / Supplements Y ☐ N ☐

Eat slow ? Y ☐ N ☐

Stop when full ? Y ☐ N ☐

Tip

'Comfort food' definition: Any food that you reach out to eat or binge on, which is out of your regular food plan, or, a food that you eat to temporarily satisfy an emotion, which usually results in you feeling guilty.

Did you eat any "comfort food"?

Y ☐ N ☐

If Yes -
mention the comfort food

What were you feeling at that time?

Cause? (Person, Situation, please mention)

How did you feel after this

Exercise Notes

Activity	Minutes	Intensity			Calories Burnt
		Low	Medium	High	
☐ Elliptical					
☐ Walk					
☐ Run / Jog					
☐ Weights					
☐ Swim					
☐ Yoga					
☐ Pilates					
☐ Cycle					
☐ Martial Arts					
☐ Kick Boxing					
☐ Sport					

retching / Warm up Y ☐ N ☐

ainer / Instructor Y ☐ N ☐

"The starting point of all achievement is desire" - Napolean Hill

Comments: (Problem, Injuries, Overall mood, Best/worst moment, Etc...)

minders:

....

....

Met today's goals?

0% 25% 50% 75% 100%

Date:		Week: #		Day: #		Day of week:	

No. of hours sleep (previous night)

Food Notes

Upon waking

Time:

Breakfast

Time:

Snack 1

Time:

Lunch

Time:

Snack 2

Time:

Snack 3

Time:

Dinner

Time:

Before Sleep

Time:

Water ☐ ☐ ☐ ☐ ☐ ☐ ☐ ☐ ☐
☐ ☐ ☐ ☐ ☐ ☐ ☐ ☐ ☐

Vitamins / Supplements Y ☐ N ☐

Eat slow ? Y ☐ N ☐

Stop when full ? Y ☐ N ☐

Tip

Eat Small Meals Every 3 Hours. This Will Boost Your Metabolism and Turn Your Body Into a Fat Burning Machine.

Did you eat any "comfort food"?

Y ☐ N ☐

If Yes -
mention the comfort food

What were you feeling at that time?

Cause? (Person, Situation, please mention)

How did you feel after this?

Exercise Notes

Activity	Minutes	Intensity			Calories Burnt
		Low	Medium	High	
☐ Elliptical					
☐ Walk					
☐ Run / Jog					
☐ Weights					
☐ Swim					
☐ Yoga					
☐ Pilates					
☐ Cycle					
☐ Martial Arts					
☐ Kick Boxing					
☐ Sport					

etching / Warm up Y ☐ N ☐

iner / Instructor Y ☐ N ☐

Under promise. Over Deliver.

Comments: (Problem, Injuries, Overall mood, Best/worst moment, Etc...)

minders:

....

....

Met today's goals?

0% 25% 50% 75% 100%

Date: | Week: # | Day: # | Day of week:

No. of hours sleep (previous night)

Food Notes

Upon waking

Time:

Breakfast

Time:

Snack 1

Time:

Lunch

Time:

Snack 2

Time:

Snack 3

Time:

Dinner

Time:

Before Sleep

Time:

Water ☐ ☐ ☐ ☐ ☐ ☐ ☐ ☐ ☐
☐ ☐ ☐ ☐ ☐ ☐ ☐ ☐ ☐

Vitamins / Supplements Y ☐ N ☐

Eat slow ? Y ☐ N ☐

Stop when full ? Y ☐ N ☐

Tip

Drink Loads of Water. It's the elixir of life.

Did you eat any "comfort food"?

Y ☐ N ☐

If Yes -
mention the comfort food

What were you feeling at that time?

Cause? (Person, Situation, please mention)

How did you feel after this?

Exercise Notes

ctivity	Minutes	Intensity			Calories Burnt
		Low	Medium	High	
] Elliptical					
] Walk					
] Run / Jog					
] Weights					
] Swim					
] Yoga					
] Pilates					
Cycle					
Martial Arts					
Kick Boxing					
Sport					

tching / Warm up Y ☐ N ☐

ner / Instructor Y ☐ N ☐

"Fortes Fortuna Adiouat" Fortune Favors The Bold.

Comments: (Problem, Injuries, Overall mood, Best/worst moment, Etc...)

ninders:

Met today's goals?

0% 25% 50% 75% 100%

Date: | Week: # | Day: # | Day of week:

No. of hours sleep (previous night)

Food Notes

Upon waking

Time:

Breakfast

Time:

Snack 1

Time:

Lunch

Time:

Snack 2

Time:

Snack 3

Time:

Dinner

Time:

Before Sleep

Time:

Water ☐ ☐ ☐ ☐ ☐ ☐ ☐ ☐ ☐
☐ ☐ ☐ ☐ ☐ ☐ ☐ ☐ ☐

Vitamins / Supplements Y ☐ N ☐

Eat slow ? Y ☐ N ☐

Stop when full ? Y ☐ N ☐

Tip

Comfort food is usually rich in carbohydrates, sugars and saturated oils. They are usually packed and processed foods, rich in sodium and preservatives.

Did you eat any "comfort food"?

Y ☐ N ☐

If Yes -
mention the comfort food

What were you feeling at that time?

Cause? (Person, Situation, please mention)

How did you feel after this?

Exercise Notes

ctivity	Minutes	Intensity			Calories Burnt
		Low	Medium	High	
] Elliptical					
] Walk					
] Run / Jog					
] Weights					
] Swim					
] Yoga					
Pilates					
Cycle					
Martial Arts					
Kick Boxing					
Sport					

tching / Warm up Y ☐ N ☐

ner / Instructor Y ☐ N ☐

"Impossible is nothing"

Comments: (Problem, Injuries, Overall mood, Best/worst moment, Etc...)

inders:

....

....

Met today's goals?

0% 25% 50% 75% 100%

Date: | Week: # | Day: # | Day of week:

No. of hours sleep (previous night)

Food Notes

Upon waking

Time:

Breakfast

Time:

Snack 1

Time:

Lunch

Time:

Snack 2

Time:

Snack 3

Time:

Dinner

Time:

Before Sleep

Time:

Water ☐ ☐ ☐ ☐ ☐ ☐ ☐ ☐ ☐
☐ ☐ ☐ ☐ ☐ ☐ ☐ ☐ ☐

Vitamins / Supplements Y ☐ N ☐

Eat slow ? Y ☐ N ☐

Stop when full ? Y ☐ N ☐

Tip

Experiment with green tea. It's rich in antioxidants and is a natural slimming agent.

Did you eat any "comfort food"?

Y ☐ N ☐

If Yes -
mention the comfort food

What were you feeling at that time?

Cause? (Person, Situation, please mention)

How did you feel after this

Exercise Notes

Activity	Minutes	Intensity			Calories Burnt
		Low	Medium	High	
☐ Elliptical					
☐ Walk					
☐ Run / Jog					
☐ Weights					
☐ Swim					
☐ Yoga					
☐ Pilates					
☐ Cycle					
☐ Martial Arts					
☐ Kick Boxing					
☐ Sport					

retching / Warm up Y ☐ N ☐

ainer / Instructor Y ☐ N ☐

"Your attempt may fail, but never fail to make an attempt"

Comments: (Problem, Injuries, Overall mood, Best/worst moment, Etc...)

minders:

....

....

Met today's goals?

0% 25% 50% 75% 100%

Date: | Week: # | Day: # | Day of week:

No. of hours sleep (previous night)

Food Notes

Upon waking

Time:

Breakfast

Time:

Snack 1

Time:

Lunch

Time:

Snack 2

Time:

Snack 3

Time:

Dinner

Time:

Before Sleep

Time:

Water ☐ ☐ ☐ ☐ ☐ ☐ ☐ ☐ ☐
☐ ☐ ☐ ☐ ☐ ☐ ☐ ☐ ☐

Vitamins / Supplements Y ☐ N ☐

Eat slow ? Y ☐ N ☐

Stop when full ? Y ☐ N ☐

Tip

Sugar is your enemy. It's an "empty calorie" that pollutes your body. Switch to honey or other natural sugars.

Did you eat any "comfort food"?

Y ☐ N ☐

If Yes -
mention the comfort food

What were you feeling at that time?

Cause? (Person, Situation, please mention)

How did you feel after this?

Exercise Notes

Activity	Minutes	Intensity			Calories Burnt
		Low	Medium	High	
☐ Elliptical					
☐ Walk					
☐ Run / Jog					
☐ Weights					
☐ Swim					
☐ Yoga					
☐ Pilates					
☐ Cycle					
☐ Martial Arts					
☐ Kick Boxing					
☐ Sport					

etching / Warm up Y ☐ N ☐

iner / Instructor Y ☐ N ☐

"When the going gets tough, the tough get going"

Comments: (Problem, Injuries, Overall mood, Best/worst moment, Etc...)

minders:

....

....

Met today's goals?

0% 25% 50% 75% 100%

Date: | Week: # | Day: # | Day of week:

No. of hours sleep (previous night)

Food Notes

Upon waking

Time:

Breakfast

Time:

Snack 1

Time:

Lunch

Time:

Snack 2

Time:

Snack 3

Time:

Dinner

Time:

Before Sleep

Time:

Tip

Keep a gap of atleast 2 hours between dinner and sleep. Allow for your dinner to digest completely.

Did you eat any "comfort food"?

Y ☐ N ☐

If Yes - mention the comfort food

What were you feeling at that time?

Cause? (Person, Situation, please mention)

How did you feel after this?

Water ☐ ☐ ☐ ☐ ☐ ☐ ☐ ☐ ☐
☐ ☐ ☐ ☐ ☐ ☐ ☐ ☐ ☐

Vitamins / Supplements Y ☐ N ☐

Eat slow ? Y ☐ N ☐

Stop when full ? Y ☐ N ☐

Exercise Notes

ctivity	Minutes	Intensity			Calories Burnt
		Low	Medium	High	
] Elliptical					
] Walk					
] Run / Jog					
] Weights					
] Swim					
] Yoga					
] Pilates					
] Cycle					
] Martial Arts					
] Kick Boxing					
] Sport					

etching / Warm up Y ☐ N ☐

iner / Instructor Y ☐ N ☐

"When the winds of change blow, some people build walls and others windmills"
- Attitude Matters

Comments: (Problem, Injuries, Overall mood, Best/worst moment, Etc...)

ninders:

Met today's goals?

0% 25% 50% 75% 100%

Your Scribble Space

(Take your favorite color pen, crayon, pencil and scribble happy thoughts, words, and feelings below, or just paste a picture of someone you love and care about. This is your space, make it happy, vibrant and colorful.)

Last week's happiest moment ____________________

Not so good moment ____________________

Something nice that someone said to you ____________________

Something nice that you said to or did for someone ____________________

Something special you want to do for someone next week ____________________

Are you happy and motivated to stay healthy and fit ? (if not mention why) ____________________

A reward you want to give yourself for staying on track with your fitness goals ____________________

Weekly Goals __________________ ____________________

Plan Your Week

	Mon	Tue	Wed	Thur	Fri	Sat	Sun
xercise							
wim							
Valk							
un							
lliptical							
ycle							
Veights							
ports							
oga							
ther:							
est day							
ood							
at outs							
rder in							
etox							
eligious fast							
eep							
Hours							
Hours							
7 Hours							
assage							

These are your goals for the week. Strive to achieve them.

"A goal without an action plan, is a dream"

Date: | Week: # | Day: # | Day of week:

No. of hours sleep (previous night)

Food Notes

Upon waking

Time:

Breakfast

Time:

Snack 1

Time:

Lunch

Time:

Snack 2

Time:

Snack 3

Time:

Dinner

Time:

Before Sleep

Time:

Water ☐ ☐ ☐ ☐ ☐ ☐ ☐ ☐ ☐
☐ ☐ ☐ ☐ ☐ ☐ ☐ ☐ ☐

Vitamins / Supplements Y ☐ N ☐

Eat slow ? Y ☐ N ☐

Stop when full ? Y ☐ N ☐

Tip

Chew your food, connect with it and understand its flavours. Enjoy what you eat.

Did you eat any "comfort food"?

Y ☐ N ☐

If Yes -
mention the comfort food

What were you feeling at that time?

Cause? (Person, Situation, please mention)

How did you feel after this

Exercise Notes

Activity	Minutes	Intensity			Calories Burnt
		Low	Medium	High	
☐ Elliptical					
☐ Walk					
☐ Run / Jog					
☐ Weights					
☐ Swim					
☐ Yoga					
☐ Pilates					
☐ Cycle					
☐ Martial Arts					
☐ Kick Boxing					
☐ Sport					

retching / Warm up Y ☐ N ☐

ainer / Instructor Y ☐ N ☐

"The only place where our dreams become impossible, is in our own thinking."

Comments: (Problem, Injuries, Overall mood, Best/worst moment, Etc...)

minders:

....

....

Met today's goals?

0% 25% 50% 75% 100%

Date: | Week: # | Day: # | Day of week:

No. of hours sleep (previous night)

Food Notes

Upon waking

Time:

Breakfast

Time:

Snack 1

Time:

Lunch

Time:

Snack 2

Time:

Snack 3

Time:

Dinner

Time:

Before Sleep

Time:

Water ☐ ☐ ☐ ☐ ☐ ☐ ☐ ☐ ☐
☐ ☐ ☐ ☐ ☐ ☐ ☐ ☐ ☐

Vitamins / Supplements Y ☐ N ☐

Eat slow ? Y ☐ N ☐

Stop when full ? Y ☐ N ☐

Tip

If you're hungry, eat, but make sure it's physical and not emotional hunger.

Did you eat any "comfort food"?

Y ☐ N ☐

If Yes -
mention the comfort food

What were you feeling at that time?

Cause? (Person, Situation, please mention)

How did you feel after this?

Exercise Notes

Activity	Minutes	Intensity			Calories Burnt
		Low	Medium	High	
☐ Elliptical					
☐ Walk					
☐ Run / Jog					
☐ Weights					
☐ Swim					
☐ Yoga					
☐ Pilates					
☐ Cycle					
☐ Martial Arts					
☐ Kick Boxing					
☐ Sport					

etching / Warm up Y ☐ N ☐

iner / Instructor Y ☐ N ☐

**"Do not lower your goals to the level of your abilities.
Raise your abilities to the height of your goals"**

Comments: (Problem, Injuries, Overall mood, Best/worst moment, Etc...)

ninders:

....

....

Met today's goals?

0% 25% 50% 75% 100%

Date: | Week: # | Day: # | Day of week:

No. of hours sleep (previous night)

Food Notes

Upon waking

Time:

Breakfast

Time:

Snack 1

Time:

Lunch

Time:

Snack 2

Time:

Snack 3

Time:

Dinner

Time:

Before Sleep

Time:

Water ☐ ☐ ☐ ☐ ☐ ☐ ☐ ☐ ☐
☐ ☐ ☐ ☐ ☐ ☐ ☐ ☐ ☐

Vitamins / Supplements Y ☐ N ☐

Eat slow ? Y ☐ N ☐

Stop when full ? Y ☐ N ☐

Tip

Eat a variety of nutrient rich foods. Make these relations from the food pyramid.

Did you eat any "comfort food"?

Y ☐ N ☐

If Yes -
mention the comfort food

What were you feeling at that time?

Cause? (Person, Situation, please mention)

How did you feel after this?

Exercise Notes

ctivity	Minutes	Intensity			Calories Burnt
		Low	Medium	High	
] Elliptical					
] Walk					
] Run / Jog					
] Weights					
] Swim					
] Yoga					
] Pilates					
] Cycle					
] Martial Arts					
] Kick Boxing					
] Sport					

etching / Warm up Y ☐ N ☐

ner / Instructor Y ☐ N ☐

"Success is not measured by how well you fulfil the expectations of others, but how HONESTLY you live up to your own expectation."

Comments: (Problem, Injuries, Overall mood, Best/worst moment, Etc...)

ninders:

Met today's goals?

0% 25% 50% 75% 100%

Date: | Week: # | Day: # | Day of week:

No. of hours sleep (previous night)

Food Notes

Upon waking

Time:

Breakfast

Time:

Snack 1

Time:

Lunch

Time:

Snack 2

Time:

Snack 3

Time:

Dinner

Time:

Before Sleep

Time:

Water ☐ ☐ ☐ ☐ ☐ ☐ ☐ ☐ ☐
☐ ☐ ☐ ☐ ☐ ☐ ☐ ☐ ☐

Vitamins / Supplements Y ☐ N ☐

Eat slow ? Y ☐ N ☐

Stop when full ? Y ☐ N ☐

Tip

Eat plenty of whole grains, fruits, vegetables.

Did you eat any "comfort food"?

Y ☐ N ☐

If Yes - mention the comfort food

What were you feeling at that time?

Cause? (Person, Situation, please mention)

How did you feel after this?

Exercise Notes

ctivity	Minutes	Intensity			Calories Burnt
		Low	Medium	High	
] Elliptical					
] Walk					
] Run / Jog					
] Weights					
Swim					
Yoga					
Pilates					
Cycle					
Martial Arts					
Kick Boxing					
Sport					

tching / Warm up Y ☐ N ☐

ner / Instructor Y ☐ N ☐

"There is always a substitute for everything."

Comments: (Problem, Injuries, Overall mood, Best/worst moment, Etc...)

nders:

Met today's goals?

0% 25% 50% 75% 100%

Date: | Week: # | Day: # | Day of week:

No. of hours sleep (previous night)

Food Notes

Upon waking

Time:

Breakfast

Time:

Snack 1

Time:

Lunch

Time:

Snack 2

Time:

Snack 3

Time:

Dinner

Time:

Before Sleep

Time:

Water ☐ ☐ ☐ ☐ ☐ ☐ ☐ ☐ ☐
☐ ☐ ☐ ☐ ☐ ☐ ☐ ☐ ☐

Vitamins / Supplements Y ☐ N ☐

Eat slow ? Y ☐ N ☐

Stop when full ? Y ☐ N ☐

Tip

Reduce, don't eliminate certain foods.

Did you eat any "comfort food"?

Y ☐ N ☐

If Yes -
mention the comfort food

What were you feeling at that time?

Cause? (Person, Situation, please mention)

How did you feel after this

Exercise Notes

Activity	Minutes	Intensity			Calories Burnt
		Low	Medium	High	
☐ Elliptical					
☐ Walk					
☐ Run / Jog					
☐ Weights					
☐ Swim					
☐ Yoga					
☐ Pilates					
☐ Cycle					
☐ Martial Arts					
☐ Kick Boxing					
☐ Sport					

retching / Warm up Y ☐ N ☐

ainer / Instructor Y ☐ N ☐

"When people get old and look back on their lives,
they tend to regret the thing they didn't do, versus the thing they did."

Comments: (Problem, Injuries, Overall mood, Best/worst moment, Etc...)

minders:

....

....

Met today's goals?

☐☐☐☐

0% 25% 50% 75% 100%

Date: | Week: # | Day: # | Day of week:

No. of hours sleep (previous night)

Food Notes

Upon waking

Time:

Breakfast

Time:

Snack 1

Time:

Lunch

Time:

Snack 2

Time:

Snack 3

Time:

Dinner

Time:

Before Sleep

Time:

Water ☐ ☐ ☐ ☐ ☐ ☐ ☐ ☐ ☐
☐ ☐ ☐ ☐ ☐ ☐ ☐ ☐ ☐

Vitamins / Supplements Y ☐ N ☐

Eat slow ? Y ☐ N ☐

Stop when full ? Y ☐ N ☐

Tip

Limit processed and packaged foods. Move closer to nature and its offerings.

Did you eat any "comfort food"?

Y ☐ N ☐

If Yes -
mention the comfort food

What were you feeling at that time?

Cause? (Person, Situation, please mention)

How did you feel after this?

Exercise Notes

Activity	Minutes	Intensity			Calories Burnt
		Low	Medium	High	
☐ Elliptical					
☐ Walk					
☐ Run / Jog					
☐ Weights					
☐ Swim					
☐ Yoga					
☐ Pilates					
☐ Cycle					
☐ Martial Arts					
☐ Kick Boxing					
☐ Sport					

etching / Warm up Y ☐ N ☐

iner / Instructor Y ☐ N ☐

"I am healthy, happy and radiant. Am I?"

Comments: (Problem, Injuries, Overall mood, Best/worst moment, Etc...)

minders:

....

....

Met today's goals?

0%	25%	50%	75%	100%

Date: | Week: # | Day: # | Day of week:

No. of hours sleep (previous night)

Food Notes

Upon waking

Time:

Breakfast

Time:

Snack 1

Time:

Lunch

Time:

Snack 2

Time:

Snack 3

Time:

Dinner

Time:

Before Sleep

Time:

Water ☐ ☐ ☐ ☐ ☐ ☐ ☐ ☐ ☐
☐ ☐ ☐ ☐ ☐ ☐ ☐ ☐ ☐

Vitamins / Supplements Y ☐ N ☐

Eat slow ? Y ☐ N ☐

Stop when full ? Y ☐ N ☐

Tip

Feeling tired? Review your sleep time and what you eat. Food is fuel to your body.

Did you eat any "comfort food"?

Y ☐ N ☐

If Yes - mention the comfort food

What were you feeling at that time?

Cause? (Person, Situation, please mention)

How did you feel after this?

Exercise Notes

ctivity	Minutes	Intensity			Calories Burnt
		Low	Medium	High	
] Elliptical					
] Walk					
] Run / Jog					
] Weights					
] Swim					
] Yoga					
] Pilates					
] Cycle					
] Martial Arts					
Kick Boxing					
Sport					

tching / Warm up Y ☐ N ☐

ner / Instructor Y ☐ N ☐

"If you had to name the one most important ingredient of Human beauty, what would you say it is?"

Comments: (Problem, Injuries, Overall mood, Best/worst moment, Etc...)

ninders:

Met today's goals?

0% 25% 50% 75% 100%

Your Scribble Space

(Take your favorite color pen, crayon, pencil and scribble happy thoughts, words, and feelings below, or just paste a picture of someone you love and care about. This is your space, make it happy, vibrant and colorful.)

Last week's happiest moment ______________________________

Not so good moment ______________________________

Something nice that someone said to you ______________________________

Something nice that you said to or did for someone ______________________________

Something special you want to do for someone next week ______________________________

Are you happy and motivated to stay healthy and fit ? (if not mention why) ______________________________

A reward you want to give yourself for staying on track with your fitness goals ______________________________

Weekly Goals ______________ ______________

Plan Your Week

	Mon	Tue	Wed	Thur	Fri	Sat	Sun
:xercise							
;wim							
Valk							
:un							
lliptical							
:ycle							
Veights							
ports							
oga							
ther:							
est day							
ood							
at outs							
rder in							
etox							
eligious fast							
eep							
Hours							
Hours							
7 Hours							
assage							

These are your goals for the week. Strive to achieve them.
"A goal without an action plan, is a dream"

Date:	Week: #	Day: #	Day of week:

No. of hours sleep (previous night)

Food Notes

Upon waking

Time:

Breakfast

Time:

Snack 1

Time:

Lunch

Time:

Snack 2

Time:

Snack 3

Time:

Dinner

Time:

Before Sleep

Time:

Tip

Never skip breakfast. It's the most important meal of the day. You need breakfast to jumpstart your metabolism.

Did you eat any "comfort food"?

Y ☐ N ☐

If Yes -
mention the comfort food

What were you feeling at that time?

Cause? (Person, Situation, please mention)

How did you feel after this

Water ☐ ☐ ☐ ☐ ☐ ☐ ☐ ☐ ☐
☐ ☐ ☐ ☐ ☐ ☐ ☐ ☐ ☐

Vitamins / Supplements Y ☐ N ☐

Eat slow ? Y ☐ N ☐

Stop when full ? Y ☐ N ☐

Exercise Notes

Activity	Minutes	Intensity			Calories Burnt
		Low	Medium	High	
☐ Elliptical					
☐ Walk					
☐ Run / Jog					
☐ Weights					
☐ Swim					
☐ Yoga					
☐ Pilates					
☐ Cycle					
☐ Martial Arts					
☐ Kick Boxing					
☐ Sport					

retching / Warm up Y ☐ N ☐

ainer / Instructor Y ☐ N ☐

"The greatest wealth is health" - Virgil

Comments: (Problem, Injuries, Overall mood, Best/worst moment, Etc...)

minders:

....

....

Met today's goals?

0% 25% 50% 75% 100%

Date: | Week: # | Day: # | Day of week:

No. of hours sleep (previous night)

Food Notes

Upon waking

Time:

Breakfast

Time:

Snack 1

Time:

Lunch

Time:

Snack 2

Time:

Snack 3

Time:

Dinner

Time:

Before Sleep

Time:

Water ☐ ☐ ☐ ☐ ☐ ☐ ☐ ☐ ☐
☐ ☐ ☐ ☐ ☐ ☐ ☐ ☐ ☐

Vitamins / Supplements Y ☐ N ☐

Eat slow ? Y ☐ N ☐

Stop when full ? Y ☐ N ☐

Tip

Eat foods rich in anti-oxidants. They are known to prevent cancer.

Did you eat any "comfort food"?

Y ☐ N ☐

If Yes - mention the comfort food

What were you feeling at that time?

Cause? (Person, Situation, please mention)

How did you feel after this?

Exercise Notes

Activity	Minutes	Intensity			Calories Burnt
		Low	Medium	High	
☐ Elliptical					
☐ Walk					
☐ Run / Jog					
☐ Weights					
☐ Swim					
☐ Yoga					
☐ Pilates					
☐ Cycle					
☐ Martial Arts					
☐ Kick Boxing					
☐ Sport					

etching / Warm up Y ☐ N ☐

iner / Instructor Y ☐ N ☐

"Health is a state of complete physical and social well being and not merely the absence of disease or infirmity" - WHO

Comments: (Problem, Injuries, Overall mood, Best/worst moment, Etc...)

minders:

Met today's goals?

0% 25% 50% 75% 100%

Date: | Week: # | Day: # | Day of week:

No. of hours sleep (previous night)

Food Notes

Upon waking

Time:

Breakfast

Time:

Snack 1

Time:

Lunch

Time:

Snack 2

Time:

Snack 3

Time:

Dinner

Time:

Before Sleep

Time:

Water ☐ ☐ ☐ ☐ ☐ ☐ ☐ ☐ ☐
☐ ☐ ☐ ☐ ☐ ☐ ☐ ☐ ☐

Vitamins / Supplements Y ☐ N ☐

Eat slow ? Y ☐ N ☐

Stop when full ? Y ☐ N ☐

Tip

Always eat a fruit before you have your cup of tea or coffee in the morning.

Did you eat any "comfort food"?

Y ☐ N ☐

If Yes -
mention the comfort food

What were you feeling at that time?

Cause? (Person, Situation, please mention)

How did you feel after this?

Exercise Notes

ctivity	Minutes	Intensity			Calories Burnt
		Low	Medium	High	
Elliptical					
Walk					
Run / Jog					
Weights					
Swim					
Yoga					
Pilates					
Cycle					
Martial Arts					
Kick Boxing					
Sport					

tching / Warm up Y ☐ N ☐

ner / Instructor Y ☐ N ☐

"In order to change, we should be sick and tired of being sick and tired"

Comments: (Problem, Injuries, Overall mood, Best/worst moment, Etc...)

iinders:

....

....

Met today's goals?

0% 25% 50% 75% 100%

Date: | Week: # | Day: # | Day of week:

No. of hours sleep (previous night)

Food Notes

Upon waking

Time:

Breakfast

Time:

Snack 1

Time:

Lunch

Time:

Snack 2

Time:

Snack 3

Time:

Dinner

Time:

Before Sleep

Time:

Water ☐ ☐ ☐ ☐ ☐ ☐ ☐ ☐ ☐
☐ ☐ ☐ ☐ ☐ ☐ ☐ ☐ ☐

Vitamins / Supplements Y ☐ N ☐

Eat slow ? Y ☐ N ☐

Stop when full ? Y ☐ N ☐

Tip

Explore the health benefits of nuts and seeds. These foods are rich in protein, fiber, good fats, vitamins and minerals.

Did you eat any "comfort food"?

Y ☐ N ☐

If Yes -
mention the comfort food

What were you feeling at that time?

Cause? (Person, Situation, please mention)

How did you feel after this?

Exercise Notes

ctivity	Minutes	Intensity			Calories Burnt
		Low	Medium	High	
] Elliptical					
] Walk					
] Run / Jog					
] Weights					
] Swim					
] Yoga					
Pilates					
Cycle					
Martial Arts					
Kick Boxing					
Sport					

tching / Warm up Y ☐ N ☐

ner / Instructor Y ☐ N ☐

"Six best doctors anywhere are sunshine, water, rest, air, exercise and diet."

Comments: (Problem, Injuries, Overall mood, Best/worst moment, Etc...)

inders:

....

....

Met today's goals?

0% 25% 50% 75% 100%

Date: | Week: # | Day: # | Day of week:

No. of hours sleep (previous night)

Food Notes

Upon waking

Time:

Breakfast

Time:

Snack 1

Time:

Lunch

Time:

Snack 2

Time:

Snack 3

Time:

Dinner

Time:

Before Sleep

Time:

Water ☐ ☐ ☐ ☐ ☐ ☐ ☐ ☐ ☐
☐ ☐ ☐ ☐ ☐ ☐ ☐ ☐ ☐

Vitamins / Supplements Y ☐ N ☐

Eat slow ? Y ☐ N ☐

Stop when full ? Y ☐ N ☐

Tip

Smoking will affect your health. Cut down or stop smoking before it harms you.

Did you eat any "comfort food"?

Y ☐ N ☐

If Yes -
mention the comfort food

What were you feeling at that time?

Cause? (Person, Situation, please mention)

How did you feel after this

Exercise Notes

Activity	Minutes	Intensity			Calories Burnt
		Low	Medium	High	
☐ Elliptical					
☐ Walk					
☐ Run / Jog					
☐ Weights					
☐ Swim					
☐ Yoga					
☐ Pilates					
☐ Cycle					
☐ Martial Arts					
☐ Kick Boxing					
☐ Sport					

retching / Warm up Y ☐ N ☐

ainer / Instructor Y ☐ N ☐

"If I'd know I was going to live so long, I'd have taken better care of myself"
- Leon Eldred

Comments: (Problem, Injuries, Overall mood, Best/worst moment, Etc...)

minders:

....

....

Met today's goals?

0% 25% 50% 75% 100%

Date:	Week: #	Day: #	Day of week:
		No. of hours sleep (previous night)	

Food Notes

Upon waking

Time:

Breakfast

Time:

Snack 1

Time:

Lunch

Time:

Snack 2

Time:

Snack 3

Time:

Dinner

Time:

Before Sleep

Time:

Water ☐ ☐ ☐ ☐ ☐ ☐ ☐ ☐ ☐
☐ ☐ ☐ ☐ ☐ ☐ ☐ ☐ ☐

Vitamins / Supplements Y ☐ N ☐

Eat slow ? Y ☐ N ☐

Stop when full ? Y ☐ N ☐

Tip

Spices fire up your metabolism and make your food taste good. Use them.

Did you eat any "comfort food"?

Y ☐ N ☐

If Yes -
mention the comfort food

What were you feeling at that time?

Cause? (Person, Situation, please mention)

How did you feel after this?

Exercise Notes

Activity	Minutes	Intensity			Calories Burnt
		Low	Medium	High	
☐ Elliptical					
☐ Walk					
☐ Run / Jog					
☐ Weights					
☐ Swim					
☐ Yoga					
☐ Pilates					
☐ Cycle					
☐ Martial Arts					
☐ Kick Boxing					
☐ Sport					

etching / Warm up Y ☐ N ☐

iner / Instructor Y ☐ N ☐

"The patient should be made to understand that he or she must take charge of his own life. Don't take your body to the doctor as if he were a repair shop" - Quentine

Comments: (Problem, Injuries, Overall mood, Best/worst moment, Etc...)

minders:

Met today's goals?

0% 25% 50% 75% 100%

Date: | Week: # | Day: # | Day of week:

No. of hours sleep (previous night)

Food Notes

Upon waking

Time:

Breakfast

Time:

Snack 1

Time:

Lunch

Time:

Snack 2

Time:

Snack 3

Time:

Dinner

Time:

Before Sleep

Time:

Water ☐ ☐ ☐ ☐ ☐ ☐ ☐ ☐ ☐
☐ ☐ ☐ ☐ ☐ ☐ ☐ ☐ ☐

Vitamins / Supplements Y ☐ N ☐

Eat slow ? Y ☐ N ☐

Stop when full ? Y ☐ N ☐

Tip

Papaya - A miracle fruit. Rich in vitamins and nutrients. Improves yours overall health.

Did you eat any "comfort food"?

Y ☐ N ☐

If Yes - mention the comfort food

What were you feeling at that time?

Cause? (Person, Situation, please mention)

How did you feel after this?

Exercise Notes

ctivity	Minutes	Intensity			Calories Burnt
		Low	Medium	High	
] Elliptical					
Walk					
] Run / Jog					
Weights					
Swim					
Yoga					
Pilates					
Cycle					
Martial Arts					
Kick Boxing					
Sport					

tching / Warm up Y ☐ N ☐

ner / Instructor Y ☐ N ☐

good laugh and a long sleep are the best cures in the doctors book" - Irish Proverb

Comments: (Problem, Injuries, Overall mood, Best/worst moment, Etc...)

ninders:

Met today's goals?

0% 25% 50% 75% 100%

Your Scribble Space

(Take your favorite color pen, crayon, pencil and scribble happy thoughts, words, and feelings below, or just paste a picture of someone you love and care about. This is your space, make it happy, vibrant and colorful.)

Last week's happiest moment ______________________

Not so good moment ______________________

Something nice that someone said to you ______________________

Something nice that you said to or did for someone ______________________

Something special you want to do for someone next week ______________________

Are you happy and motivated to stay healthy and fit ? (if not mention why) ______________________

A reward you want to give yourself for staying on track with your fitness goals ______________________

Weekly Goals ______________ ______________

Plan Your Week

	Mon	Tue	Wed	Thur	Fri	Sat	Sun
xercise							
wim							
Valk							
un							
lliptical							
ycle							
Veights							
ports							
oga							
ther:							
est day							
ood							
at outs							
rder in							
etox							
eligious fast							
eep							
Hours							
Hours							
7 Hours							
assage							

These are your goals for the week. Strive to achieve them.
"A goal without an action plan, is a dream"

Date: | Week: # | Day: # | Day of week:

No. of hours sleep (previous night)

Food Notes

Upon waking

Time:

Breakfast

Time:

Snack 1

Time:

Lunch

Time:

Snack 2

Time:

Snack 3

Time:

Dinner

Time:

Before Sleep

Time:

Water ☐ ☐ ☐ ☐ ☐ ☐ ☐ ☐ ☐
☐ ☐ ☐ ☐ ☐ ☐ ☐ ☐ ☐

Vitamins / Supplements Y ☐ N ☐

Eat slow ? Y ☐ N ☐

Stop when full ? Y ☐ N ☐

Tip

Don't workout on an empty stomach. Don't eat too much either before a workout.

Did you eat any "comfort food"?

Y ☐ N ☐

If Yes -
mention the comfort food

What were you feeling at that time?

Cause? (Person, Situation, please mention)

How did you feel after this

Exercise Notes

Activity	Minutes	Intensity			Calories Burnt
		Low	Medium	High	
☐ Elliptical					
☐ Walk					
☐ Run / Jog					
☐ Weights					
☐ Swim					
☐ Yoga					
☐ Pilates					
☐ Cycle					
☐ Martial Arts					
☐ Kick Boxing					
☐ Sport					

retching / Warm up Y ☐ N ☐

ainer / Instructor Y ☐ N ☐

"When it comes to eating right and exercising, there is no "I'll start tomorrow", tomorrow is a disease" - Terri Guillements

Comments: (Problem, Injuries, Overall mood, Best/worst moment, Etc...)

minders:

Met today's goals?

0% 25% 50% 75% 100%

Date:	Week: #	Day: #	Day of week:
		No. of hours sleep (previous night)	

Food Notes

Upon waking

Time:

Breakfast

Time:

Snack 1

Time:

Lunch

Time:

Snack 2

Time:

Snack 3

Time:

Dinner

Time:

Before Sleep

Time:

Water ☐ ☐ ☐ ☐ ☐ ☐ ☐ ☐ ☐
☐ ☐ ☐ ☐ ☐ ☐ ☐ ☐ ☐

Vitamins / Supplements Y ☐ N ☐

Eat slow ? Y ☐ N ☐

Stop when full ? Y ☐ N ☐

Tip

A whole fruit is healthier than a fruit juice.

Did you eat any "comfort food"?

Y ☐ N ☐

If Yes -
mention the comfort food

What were you feeling at that time?

Cause? (Person, Situation, please mention)

How did you feel after this?

Exercise Notes

Activity	Minutes	Intensity			Calories Burnt
		Low	Medium	High	
☐ Elliptical					
☐ Walk					
☐ Run / Jog					
☐ Weights					
☐ Swim					
☐ Yoga					
☐ Pilates					
☐ Cycle					
☐ Martial Arts					
☐ Kick Boxing					
☐ Sport					

etching / Warm up Y ☐ N ☐

iner / Instructor Y ☐ N ☐

"We drink to one another's health, and spoil our own" - Jeromek

Comments: (Problem, Injuries, Overall mood, Best/worst moment, Etc...)

ninders:

....

....

Met today's goals?

0% 25% 50% 75% 100%

Date: | Week: # | Day: # | Day of week:

No. of hours sleep (previous night)

Food Notes

Upon waking

Time:

Breakfast

Time:

Snack 1

Time:

Lunch

Time:

Snack 2

Time:

Snack 3

Time:

Dinner

Time:

Before Sleep

Time:

Water ☐ ☐ ☐ ☐ ☐ ☐ ☐ ☐ ☐
☐ ☐ ☐ ☐ ☐ ☐ ☐ ☐ ☐

Vitamins / Supplements Y ☐ N ☐

Eat slow ? Y ☐ N ☐

Stop when full ? Y ☐ N ☐

Tip

Stretch wherever you can. It keeps you supple and promotes blood circulation.

Did you eat any "comfort food"?

Y ☐ N ☐

If Yes -
mention the comfort food

What were you feeling at that time?

Cause? (Person, Situation, please mention)

How did you feel after this?

Exercise Notes

ctivity	Minutes	Intensity			Calories Burnt
		Low	Medium	High	
] Elliptical					
] Walk					
] Run / Jog					
] Weights					
] Swim					
] Yoga					
] Pilates					
] Cycle					
] Martial Arts					
] Kick Boxing					
] Sport					

etching / Warm up Y ☐ N ☐

iner / Instructor Y ☐ N ☐

ickness is the vengeance of nature for the violation of her laws" - Charlies Simmons

Comments: (Problem, Injuries, Overall mood, Best/worst moment, Etc...)

minders:

Met today's goals?

0% 25% 50% 75% 100%

Date: | Week: # | Day: # | Day of week:

No. of hours sleep (previous night)

Food Notes

Upon waking

Time:

Breakfast

Time:

Snack 1

Time:

Lunch

Time:

Snack 2

Time:

Snack 3

Time:

Dinner

Time:

Before Sleep

Time:

Water ☐ ☐ ☐ ☐ ☐ ☐ ☐ ☐ ☐
☐ ☐ ☐ ☐ ☐ ☐ ☐ ☐ ☐

Vitamins / Supplements Y ☐ N ☐

Eat slow ? Y ☐ N ☐

Stop when full ? Y ☐ N ☐

Tip

Use supplements only if you must, and under professional guidance.

Did you eat any "comfort food"?

Y ☐ N ☐

If Yes -
mention the comfort food

What were you feeling at that time?

Cause? (Person, Situation, please mention)

How did you feel after this?

Exercise Notes

Activity	Minutes	Intensity			Calories Burnt
		Low	Medium	High	
☐ Elliptical					
☐ Walk					
☐ Run / Jog					
☐ Weights					
☐ Swim					
☐ Yoga					
☐ Pilates					
☐ Cycle					
☐ Martial Arts					
☐ Kick Boxing					
☐ Sport					

etching / Warm up Y ☐ N ☐

ner / Instructor Y ☐ N ☐

"From the betterness of disease, man learns the sweetness of health."

Comments: (Problem, Injuries, Overall mood, Best/worst moment, Etc...)

ninders:

....

....

Met today's goals?

0% 25% 50% 75% 100%

Date: | Week: # | Day: # | Day of week:

No. of hours sleep (previous night)

Food Notes

Upon waking

Time:

Breakfast

Time:

Snack 1

Time:

Lunch

Time:

Snack 2

Time:

Snack 3

Time:

Dinner

Time:

Before Sleep

Time:

Water ☐ ☐ ☐ ☐ ☐ ☐ ☐ ☐ ☐
☐ ☐ ☐ ☐ ☐ ☐ ☐ ☐ ☐

Vitamins / Supplements Y ☐ N ☐

Eat slow ? Y ☐ N ☐

Stop when full ? Y ☐ N ☐

Tip

Whenever you can, choose organic foods.

Did you eat any "comfort food"?

Y ☐ N ☐

If Yes - mention the comfort food

What were you feeling at that time?

Cause? (Person, Situation, please mention)

How did you feel after this

Exercise Notes

Activity	Minutes	Intensity			Calories Burnt
		Low	Medium	High	
☐ Elliptical					
☐ Walk					
☐ Run / Jog					
☐ Weights					
☐ Swim					
☐ Yoga					
☐ Pilates					
☐ Cycle					
☐ Martial Arts					
☐ Kick Boxing					
☐ Sport					

retching / Warm up Y ☐ N ☐

ainer / Instructor Y ☐ N ☐

"I see rejection in my skin, worry in my cancers, bitterness and heat in my aching joints. I failed to take care of my mind, so now my body goes to the hospital." - Astrid Alavda

Comments: (Problem, Injuries, Overall mood, Best/worst moment, Etc...)

minders:

....

....

Met today's goals?

0% 25% 50% 75% 100%

Date: | Week: # | Day: # | Day of week:

No. of hours sleep (previous night)

Food Notes

Upon waking

Time:

Breakfast

Time:

Snack 1

Time:

Lunch

Time:

Snack 2

Time:

Snack 3

Time:

Dinner

Time:

Before Sleep

Time:

Water ☐ ☐ ☐ ☐ ☐ ☐ ☐ ☐ ☐
☐ ☐ ☐ ☐ ☐ ☐ ☐ ☐ ☐

Vitamins / Supplements Y ☐ N ☐

Eat slow ? Y ☐ N ☐

Stop when full ? Y ☐ N ☐

Tip

Limit your salt intake; it is not good for your body or your blood pressure.

Did you eat any "comfort food"?

Y ☐ N ☐

If Yes -
mention the comfort food

What were you feeling at that time?

Cause? (Person, Situation, please mention)

How did you feel after this?

Exercise Notes

Activity	Minutes	Intensity			Calories Burnt
		Low	Medium	High	
☐ Elliptical					
☐ Walk					
☐ Run / Jog					
☐ Weights					
☐ Swim					
☐ Yoga					
☐ Pilates					
☐ Cycle					
☐ Martial Arts					
☐ Kick Boxing					
☐ Sport					

etching / Warm up Y ☐ N ☐

iner / Instructor Y ☐ N ☐

"To avoid sickness, eat less; to prolong life, worry less" - Chu Hui Weng

Comments: (Problem, Injuries, Overall mood, Best/worst moment, Etc...)

minders:

....

....

Met today's goals?

0% 25% 50% 75% 100%

Date: | Week: # | Day: # | Day of week:

No. of hours sleep (previous night)

Food Notes

Upon waking

Time:

Breakfast

Time:

Snack 1

Time:

Lunch

Time:

Snack 2

Time:

Snack 3

Time:

Dinner

Time:

Before Sleep

Time:

Water ☐ ☐ ☐ ☐ ☐ ☐ ☐ ☐ ☐
☐ ☐ ☐ ☐ ☐ ☐ ☐ ☐ ☐

Vitamins / Supplements Y ☐ N ☐

Eat slow ? Y ☐ N ☐

Stop when full ? Y ☐ N ☐

Tip

Stop eating products or foods that contain refined flour and sugar.

Did you eat any "comfort food"?

Y ☐ N ☐

If Yes -
mention the comfort food

What were you feeling at that time?

Cause? (Person, Situation, please mention)

How did you feel after this?

Exercise Notes

ctivity	Minutes	Intensity			Calories Burnt
		Low	Medium	High	
] Elliptical					
] Walk					
] Run / Jog					
] Weights					
] Swim					
] Yoga					
] Pilates					
] Cycle					
] Martial Arts					
] Kick Boxing					
] Sport					

etching / Warm up Y ☐ N ☐

iner / Instructor Y ☐ N ☐

"Live in rooms full of light"

Comments: (Problem, Injuries, Overall mood, Best/worst moment, Etc...)

minders:

Met today's goals?

0% 25% 50% 75% 100%

Your Scribble Space

(Take your favorite color pen, crayon, pencil and scribble happy thoughts, words, and feelings below, or just paste a picture of someone you love and care about. This is your space, make it happy, vibrant and colorful.)

Last week's happiest moment ____________________

Not so good moment ____________________

Something nice that someone said to you ____________________

Something nice that you said to or did for someone ____________________

Something special you want to do for someone next week ____________________

Are you happy and motivated to stay healthy and fit ? (if not mention why) ____________________

A reward you want to give yourself for staying on track with your fitness goals ____________________

Weekly Goals ____________________ ____________________

Plan Your Week

	Mon	Tue	Wed	Thur	Fri	Sat	Sun
xercise							
wim							
/alk							
un							
liptical							
ycle							
'eights							
orts							
ga							
ther:							
st day							
od							
t outs							
der in							
tox							
ligious fast							
eep							
lours							
lours							
' Hours							
ssage							

These are your goals for the week. Strive to achieve them.
"A goal without an action plan, is a dream"

Date: | Week: # | Day: # | Day of week:

No. of hours sleep (previous night)

Food Notes

Upon waking

Time:

Breakfast

Time:

Snack 1

Time:

Lunch

Time:

Snack 2

Time:

Snack 3

Time:

Dinner

Time:

Before Sleep

Time:

Water ☐ ☐ ☐ ☐ ☐ ☐ ☐ ☐ ☐
☐ ☐ ☐ ☐ ☐ ☐ ☐ ☐ ☐

Vitamins / Supplements Y ☐ N ☐

Eat slow ? Y ☐ N ☐

Stop when full ? Y ☐ N ☐

Tip

Create a pleasant eating atmosphere. Don't have your meals in front of the TV.

Did you eat any "comfort food"?

Y ☐ N ☐

If Yes -
mention the comfort food

What were you feeling at that time?

Cause? (Person, Situation, please mention)

How did you feel after this

Exercise Notes

Activity	Minutes	Intensity			Calories Burnt
		Low	Medium	High	
☐ Elliptical					
☐ Walk					
☐ Run / Jog					
☐ Weights					
☐ Swim					
☐ Yoga					
☐ Pilates					
☐ Cycle					
☐ Martial Arts					
☐ Kick Boxing					
☐ Sport					

retching / Warm up Y ☐ N ☐

ainer / Instructor Y ☐ N ☐

"Half the modern drugs could well be thrown out of the window, except that the birds may eat them" - Martine Fisher

Comments: (Problem, Injuries, Overall mood, Best/worst moment, Etc...)

minders:

....

....

Met today's goals?

0%	25%	50%	75%	100%

Date: | Week: # | Day: # | Day of week:

No. of hours sleep (previous night)

Food Notes

Upon waking

Time:

Breakfast

Time:

Snack 1

Time:

Lunch

Time:

Snack 2

Time:

Snack 3

Time:

Dinner

Time:

Before Sleep

Time:

Water ☐ ☐ ☐ ☐ ☐ ☐ ☐ ☐ ☐
☐ ☐ ☐ ☐ ☐ ☐ ☐ ☐ ☐

Vitamins / Supplements Y ☐ N ☐

Eat slow ? Y ☐ N ☐

Stop when full ? Y ☐ N ☐

Tip

Today I want you to open your fridge and check out all the food that's bad for you. Substitute it with food that makes you feel good.

Did you eat any "comfort food"?

Y ☐ N ☐

If Yes -
mention the comfort food

What were you feeling at that time?

Cause? (Person, Situation, please mention)

How did you feel after this?

Exercise Notes

Activity	Minutes	Intensity			Calories Burnt
		Low	Medium	High	
☐ Elliptical					
☐ Walk					
☐ Run / Jog					
☐ Weights					
☐ Swim					
☐ Yoga					
☐ Pilates					
☐ Cycle					
☐ Martial Arts					
☐ Kick Boxing					
☐ Sport					

etching / Warm up Y ☐ N ☐

iner / Instructor Y ☐ N ☐

"He who has health, has hope. He who has hope, has Everything" - Arabic Proverb

Comments: (Problem, Injuries, Overall mood, Best/worst moment, Etc...)

minders:

Met today's goals?

0% 25% 50% 75% 100%

Date:	Week: #	Day: #	Day of week:

No. of hours sleep (previous night)

Food Notes

Upon waking

Time:

Breakfast

Time:

Snack 1

Time:

Lunch

Time:

Snack 2

Time:

Snack 3

Time:

Dinner

Time:

Before Sleep

Time:

Tip

Have you been eating slow? Remember to stop when full.

Did you eat any "comfort food"?

Y ☐ N ☐

If Yes - mention the comfort food

What were you feeling at that time?

Cause? (Person, Situation, please mention)

How did you feel after this?

Water ☐ ☐ ☐ ☐ ☐ ☐ ☐ ☐ ☐
☐ ☐ ☐ ☐ ☐ ☐ ☐ ☐ ☐

Vitamins / Supplements Y ☐ N ☐

Eat slow ? Y ☐ N ☐

Stop when full ? Y ☐ N ☐

Exercise Notes

ctivity	Minutes	Intensity			Calories Burnt
		Low	Medium	High	
] Elliptical					
] Walk					
] Run / Jog					
] Weights					
] Swim					
] Yoga					
] Pilates					
] Cycle					
] Martial Arts					
] Kick Boxing					
] Sport					

etching / Warm up Y ☐ N ☐

iner / Instructor Y ☐ N ☐

"Health is a relationship between you and your body" - Terri Guillemets

Comments: (Problem, Injuries, Overall mood, Best/worst moment, Etc...)

ninders:

Met today's goals?

0% 25% 50% 75% 100%

Date:	Week: #	Day: #	Day of week:
		No. of hours sleep (previous night)	

Food Notes

Upon waking

Time:

Breakfast

Time:

Snack 1

Time:

Lunch

Time:

Snack 2

Time:

Snack 3

Time:

Dinner

Time:

Before Sleep

Time:

Water ☐ ☐ ☐ ☐ ☐ ☐ ☐ ☐ ☐
☐ ☐ ☐ ☐ ☐ ☐ ☐ ☐ ☐

Vitamins / Supplements Y ☐ N ☐

Eat slow ? Y ☐ N ☐

Stop when full ? Y ☐ N ☐

Tip

Try steaming or grilling your foods. Get creative and make it taste good.

Did you eat any "comfort food"?

Y ☐ N ☐

If Yes -
mention the comfort food

What were you feeling at that time?

Cause? (Person, Situation, please mention)

How did you feel after this?

Exercise Notes

ctivity	Minutes	Intensity			Calories Burnt
		Low	Medium	High	
] Elliptical					
] Walk					
] Run / Jog					
] Weights					
] Swim					
] Yoga					
] Pilates					
] Cycle					
] Martial Arts					
] Kick Boxing					
] Sport					

etching / Warm up Y ☐ N ☐

ner / Instructor Y ☐ N ☐

"So many people spend their health gaining wealth, and then have to spend their wealth to regain their health" - AJ MATERI

Comments: (Problem, Injuries, Overall mood, Best/worst moment, Etc...)

inders:

Met today's goals?

0% 25% 50% 75% 100%

Date: | Week: # | Day: # | Day of week:

No. of hours sleep (previous night)

Food Notes

Upon waking

Time:

Breakfast

Time:

Snack 1

Time:

Lunch

Time:

Snack 2

Time:

Snack 3

Time:

Dinner

Time:

Before Sleep

Time:

Water ☐ ☐ ☐ ☐ ☐ ☐ ☐ ☐ ☐
☐ ☐ ☐ ☐ ☐ ☐ ☐ ☐ ☐

Vitamins / Supplements Y ☐ N ☐

Eat slow ? Y ☐ N ☐

Stop when full ? Y ☐ N ☐

Tip

I am sugar free. Are You? Your body does not need refined sugar

Did you eat any "comfort food"?

Y ☐ N ☐

If Yes -
mention the comfort food

What were you feeling at that time?

Cause? (Person, Situation, please mention)

How did you feel after this

Exercise Notes

Activity	Minutes	Intensity			Calories Burnt
		Low	Medium	High	
☐ Elliptical					
☐ Walk					
☐ Run / Jog					
☐ Weights					
☐ Swim					
☐ Yoga					
☐ Pilates					
☐ Cycle					
☐ Martial Arts					
☐ Kick Boxing					
☐ Sport					

retching / Warm up Y ☐ N ☐

ainer / Instructor Y ☐ N ☐

"Every human being is the anchor of his own health or disease." - Buddha

Comments: (Problem, Injuries, Overall mood, Best/worst moment, Etc...)

minders:

Met today's goals?

0% 25% 50% 75% 100%

Date: | Week: # | Day: # | Day of week:

No. of hours sleep (previous night)

Food Notes

Upon waking

Time:

Breakfast

Time:

Snack 1

Time:

Lunch

Time:

Snack 2

Time:

Snack 3

Time:

Dinner

Time:

Before Sleep

Time:

Water ☐ ☐ ☐ ☐ ☐ ☐ ☐ ☐ ☐
☐ ☐ ☐ ☐ ☐ ☐ ☐ ☐ ☐

Vitamins / Supplements Y ☐ N ☐

Eat slow ? Y ☐ N ☐

Stop when full ? Y ☐ N ☐

Tip

Skipping meals will not make you thin.

Did you eat any "comfort food"?

Y ☐ N ☐

If Yes - mention the comfort food

What were you feeling at that time?

Cause? (Person, Situation, please mention)

How did you feel after this?

Exercise Notes

Activity	Minutes	Intensity			Calories Burnt
		Low	Medium	High	
☐ Elliptical					
☐ Walk					
☐ Run / Jog					
☐ Weights					
☐ Swim					
☐ Yoga					
☐ Pilates					
☐ Cycle					
☐ Martial Arts					
☐ Kick Boxing					
☐ Sport					

etching / Warm up Y ☐ N ☐

iner / Instructor Y ☐ N ☐

"It is the health that is real wealth, not piece of gold and silver" - Gandhi

Comments: (Problem, Injuries, Overall mood, Best/worst moment, Etc...)

ninders:

Met today's goals?

0% 25% 50% 75% 100%

Date:	Week: #	Day: #	Day of week:
		No. of hours sleep (previous night)	

Food Notes

Upon waking

Time:

Breakfast

Time:

Snack 1

Time:

Lunch

Time:

Snack 2

Time:

Snack 3

Time:

Dinner

Time:

Before Sleep

Time:

Water ☐ ☐ ☐ ☐ ☐ ☐ ☐ ☐ ☐
☐ ☐ ☐ ☐ ☐ ☐ ☐ ☐ ☐

Vitamins / Supplements Y ☐ N ☐

Eat slow ? Y ☐ N ☐

Stop when full ? Y ☐ N ☐

Tip

Eat a variety of colored fruits and vegetables. Make your plate look pretty.

Did you eat any "comfort food"?

Y ☐ N ☐

If Yes -
mention the comfort food

What were you feeling at that time?

Cause? (Person, Situation, please mention)

How did you feel after this?

Exercise Notes

ctivity	Minutes	Intensity			Calories Burnt
		Low	Medium	High	
] Elliptical					
] Walk					
] Run / Jog					
] Weights					
] Swim					
] Yoga					
] Pilates					
] Cycle					
] Martial Arts					
] Kick Boxing					
] Sport					

etching / Warm up Y ☐ N ☐

iner / Instructor Y ☐ N ☐

"To wish to be healthy is a part of becoming healthy"

Comments: (Problem, Injuries, Overall mood, Best/worst moment, Etc...)

ninders:

Met today's goals?

0% 25% 50% 75% 100%

Your Scribble Space

(Take your favorite color pen, crayon, pencil and scribble happy thoughts, words, and feelings below, or just paste a picture of someone you love and care about. This is your space, make it happy, vibrant and colorful.)

Last week's happiest moment ____________________

Not so good moment ____________________

Something nice that someone said to you ____________________

Something nice that you said to or did for someone ____________________

Something special you want to do for someone next week ____________________

Are you happy and motivated to stay healthy and fit ? (if not mention why) ____________________

A reward you want to give yourself for staying on track with your fitness goals ____________________

Weekly Goals ____________________ ______________________

Plan Your Week

	Mon	Tue	Wed	Thur	Fri	Sat	Sun
Exercise							
Swim							
Walk							
Run							
Elliptical							
Cycle							
Weights							
ports							
Yoga							
Other:							
Rest day							
ood							
at outs							
rder in							
etox							
eligious fast							
eep							
Hours							
Hours							
7 Hours							
assage							

These are your goals for the week. Strive to achieve them.
"A goal without an action plan, is a dream"

Date: | Week: # | Day: # | Day of week:

No. of hours sleep (previous night)

Food Notes

Upon waking

Time:

Breakfast

Time:

Snack 1

Time:

Lunch

Time:

Snack 2

Time:

Snack 3

Time:

Dinner

Time:

Before Sleep

Time:

Water ☐ ☐ ☐ ☐ ☐ ☐ ☐ ☐ ☐
☐ ☐ ☐ ☐ ☐ ☐ ☐ ☐ ☐

Vitamins / Supplements Y ☐ N ☐

Eat slow ? Y ☐ N ☐

Stop when full ? Y ☐ N ☐

Tip

Super foods: Garlic, Spinach, Tomato, Prunes.

Did you eat any "comfort food"?

Y ☐ N ☐

If Yes - mention the comfort food

What were you feeling at that time?

Cause? (Person, Situation, please mention)

How did you feel after this

Exercise Notes

Activity	Minutes	Intensity			Calories Burnt
		Low	Medium	High	
☐ Elliptical					
☐ Walk					
☐ Run / Jog					
☐ Weights					
☐ Swim					
☐ Yoga					
☐ Pilates					
☐ Cycle					
☐ Martial Arts					
☐ Kick Boxing					
☐ Sport					

retching / Warm up Y ☐ N ☐

ainer / Instructor Y ☐ N ☐

"Those who think they have no time for bodily exercise will sooner or later have to find time for illness" - Edward Stonely

Comments: (Problem, Injuries, Overall mood, Best/worst moment, Etc...)

minders:

....

....

Met today's goals?

0% 25% 50% 75% 100%

Date: | Week: # | Day: # | Day of week:

No. of hours sleep (previous night)

Food Notes

Upon waking

Time:

Breakfast

Time:

Snack 1

Time:

Lunch

Time:

Snack 2

Time:

Snack 3

Time:

Dinner

Time:

Before Sleep

Time:

Water ☐ ☐ ☐ ☐ ☐ ☐ ☐ ☐ ☐
☐ ☐ ☐ ☐ ☐ ☐ ☐ ☐ ☐

Vitamins / Supplements Y ☐ N ☐

Eat slow ? Y ☐ N ☐

Stop when full ? Y ☐ N ☐

Tip

Today I will eat any food I desire, but I will eat slow and stop when full.

Did you eat any "comfort food"?

Y ☐ N ☐

If Yes - mention the comfort food

What were you feeling at that time?

Cause? (Person, Situation, please mention)

How did you feel after this?

Exercise Notes

Activity	Minutes	Intensity			Calories Burnt
		Low	Medium	High	
☐ Elliptical					
☐ Walk					
☐ Run / Jog					
☐ Weights					
☐ Swim					
☐ Yoga					
☐ Pilates					
☐ Cycle					
☐ Martial Arts					
☐ Kick Boxing					
☐ Sport					

etching / Warm up Y ☐ N ☐

iner / Instructor Y ☐ N ☐

"Fitness - If it came in a bottle, everybody would have a great body" - Cher

Comments: (Problem, Injuries, Overall mood, Best/worst moment, Etc...)

minders:

Met today's goals?

0% 25% 50% 75% 100%

Date: | Week: # | Day: # | Day of week:

No. of hours sleep (previous night)

Food Notes

Upon waking

Time:

Breakfast

Time:

Snack 1

Time:

Lunch

Time:

Snack 2

Time:

Snack 3

Time:

Dinner

Time:

Before Sleep

Time:

Water ☐ ☐ ☐ ☐ ☐ ☐ ☐ ☐ ☐
☐ ☐ ☐ ☐ ☐ ☐ ☐ ☐ ☐

Vitamins / Supplements Y ☐ N ☐

Eat slow ? Y ☐ N ☐

Stop when full ? Y ☐ N ☐

Tip

Shape your goal for today. Have you planned what you want to eat?

Did you eat any "comfort food"?

Y ☐ N ☐

If Yes - mention the comfort food

What were you feeling at that time?

Cause? (Person, Situation, please mention)

How did you feel after this?

Exercise Notes

ctivity	Minutes	Intensity			Calories Burnt
		Low	Medium	High	
] Elliptical					
] Walk					
] Run / Jog					
] Weights					
] Swim					
] Yoga					
] Pilates					
] Cycle					
] Martial Arts					
] Kick Boxing					
] Sport					

etching / Warm up Y ☐ N ☐

iner / Instructor Y ☐ N ☐

"The only exercise some people get is jumping to conclusions, running down their friends, side - stepping responsibility and pushing luck"

Comments: (Problem, Injuries, Overall mood, Best/worst moment, Etc...)

ninders:

Met today's goals?

0% 25% 50% 75% 100%

Date: | Week: # | Day: # | Day of week:

No. of hours sleep (previous night)

Food Notes

Upon waking

Time:

Breakfast

Time:

Snack 1

Time:

Lunch

Time:

Snack 2

Time:

Snack 3

Time:

Dinner

Time:

Before Sleep

Time:

Water ☐ ☐ ☐ ☐ ☐ ☐ ☐ ☐ ☐
☐ ☐ ☐ ☐ ☐ ☐ ☐ ☐ ☐

Vitamins / Supplements Y ☐ N ☐

Eat slow ? Y ☐ N ☐

Stop when full ? Y ☐ N ☐

Tip

What you practise you become. Eat wisely.

Did you eat any "comfort food"?

Y ☐ N ☐

If Yes - mention the comfort food

What were you feeling at that time?

Cause? (Person, Situation, please mention)

How did you feel after this?

Exercise Notes

Activity	Minutes	Intensity			Calories Burnt
		Low	Medium	High	
☐ Elliptical					
☐ Walk					
☐ Run / Jog					
☐ Weights					
☐ Swim					
☐ Yoga					
☐ Pilates					
☐ Cycle					
☐ Martial Arts					
☐ Kick Boxing					
☐ Sport					

etching / Warm up Y ☐ N ☐

iner / Instructor Y ☐ N ☐

"Movement is the medicine for creating change in a person's physical, emotional and mental status." - Carol Wetch

Comments: (Problem, Injuries, Overall mood, Best/worst moment, Etc...)

ninders:

....

....

Met today's goals?

0% 25% 50% 75% 100%

Date: | Week: # | Day: # | Day of week:

No. of hours sleep (previous night)

Food Notes

Upon waking

Time:

Breakfast

Time:

Snack 1

Time:

Lunch

Time:

Snack 2

Time:

Snack 3

Time:

Dinner

Time:

Before Sleep

Time:

Water ☐ ☐ ☐ ☐ ☐ ☐ ☐ ☐ ☐
☐ ☐ ☐ ☐ ☐ ☐ ☐ ☐ ☐

Vitamins / Supplements Y ☐ N ☐

Eat slow ? Y ☐ N ☐

Stop when full ? Y ☐ N ☐

Tip

Listen to your body, If you are hungry, eat.

Did you eat any "comfort food"?

Y ☐ N ☐

If Yes -
mention the comfort food

What were you feeling at that time?

Cause? (Person, Situation, please mention)

How did you feel after this

Exercise Notes

Activity	Minutes	Intensity			Calories Burnt
		Low	Medium	High	
☐ Elliptical					
☐ Walk					
☐ Run / Jog					
☐ Weights					
☐ Swim					
☐ Yoga					
☐ Pilates					
☐ Cycle					
☐ Martial Arts					
☐ Kick Boxing					
☐ Sport					

retching / Warm up Y ☐ N ☐

ainer / Instructor Y ☐ N ☐

"A man's health can be judged by which he takes two at a time - pills or stairs"
- Joon Welsh

Comments: (Problem, Injuries, Overall mood, Best/worst moment, Etc...)

minders:

....

....

Met today's goals?

0% 25% 50% 75% 100%

Date: | Week: # | Day: # | Day of week:

No. of hours sleep (previous night)

Food Notes

Upon waking

Time:

Breakfast

Time:

Snack 1

Time:

Lunch

Time:

Snack 2

Time:

Snack 3

Time:

Dinner

Time:

Before Sleep

Time:

Water ☐ ☐ ☐ ☐ ☐ ☐ ☐ ☐ ☐
☐ ☐ ☐ ☐ ☐ ☐ ☐ ☐ ☐

Vitamins / Supplements Y ☐ N ☐

Eat slow ? Y ☐ N ☐

Stop when full ? Y ☐ N ☐

Tip

Dark chocolate is good for your heart and skin.

Did you eat any "comfort food"?

Y ☐ N ☐

If Yes -
mention the comfort food

What were you feeling at that time?

Cause? (Person, Situation, please mention)

How did you feel after this?

Exercise Notes

Activity	Minutes	Intensity			Calories Burnt
		Low	Medium	High	
☐ Elliptical					
☐ Walk					
☐ Run / Jog					
☐ Weights					
☐ Swim					
☐ Yoga					
☐ Pilates					
☐ Cycle					
☐ Martial Arts					
☐ Kick Boxing					
☐ Sport					

etching / Warm up Y ☐ N ☐

iner / Instructor Y ☐ N ☐

"Commit to be fit"

Comments: (Problem, Injuries, Overall mood, Best/worst moment, Etc...)

ninders:

....

....

Met today's goals?

0% 25% 50% 75% 100%

Date:	Week: #	Day: #	Day of week:
		No. of hours sleep (previous night)	

Food Notes

Upon waking

Time:

Breakfast

Time:

Snack 1

Time:

Lunch

Time:

Snack 2

Time:

Snack 3

Time:

Dinner

Time:

Before Sleep

Time:

Tip

Breathe more,
Eat less.

Did you eat any "comfort food"?

Y ☐ N ☐

If Yes - mention the comfort food

What were you feeling at that time?

Cause? (Person, Situation, please mention)

How did you feel after this?

Water ☐ ☐ ☐ ☐ ☐ ☐ ☐ ☐ ☐
☐ ☐ ☐ ☐ ☐ ☐ ☐ ☐ ☐

Vitamins / Supplements Y ☐ N ☐

Eat slow ? Y ☐ N ☐

Stop when full ? Y ☐ N ☐

Exercise Notes

ctivity	Minutes	Intensity			Calories Burnt
		Low	Medium	High	
] Elliptical					
] Walk					
] Run / Jog					
] Weights					
] Swim					
] Yoga					
] Pilates					
] Cycle					
] Martial Arts					
] Kick Boxing					
] Sport					

etching / Warm up Y ☐ N ☐

iner / Instructor Y ☐ N ☐

"If your dog is fat you're not getting enough exercise"

Comments: (Problem, Injuries, Overall mood, Best/worst moment, Etc...)

minders:

Met today's goals?

0% 25% 50% 75% 100%

Your Scribble Space

(Take your favorite color pen, crayon, pencil and scribble happy thoughts, words, and feelings below, or just paste a picture of someone you love and care about. This is your space, make it happy, vibrant and colorful.)

Last week's happiest moment ____________________

Not so good moment ____________________

Something nice that someone said to you ____________________

Something nice that you said to or did for someone ____________________

Something special you want to do for someone next week ____________________

Are you happy and motivated to stay healthy and fit ? (if not mention why) ____________________

A reward you want to give yourself for staying on track with your fitness goals ____________________

Weekly Goals ____________________ ____________________

Plan Your Week

	Mon	Tue	Wed	Thur	Fri	Sat	Sun
xercise							
wim							
Valk							
un							
lliptical							
ycle							
Veights							
ports							
oga							
ther:							
est day							
ood							
t outs							
rder in							
etox							
ligious fast							
eep							
Hours							
Hours							
7 Hours							
assage							

These are your goals for the week. Strive to achieve them.
"A goal without an action plan, is a dream"

Date:	Week: #	Day: #	Day of week:

No. of hours sleep (previous night)

Food Notes

Upon waking

Time:

Breakfast

Time:

Snack 1

Time:

Lunch

Time:

Snack 2

Time:

Snack 3

Time:

Dinner

Time:

Before Sleep

Time:

Tip

Today is a gift. How do you plan to use it?

Did you eat any "comfort food"?

Y ☐ N ☐

If Yes - mention the comfort food

What were you feeling at that time?

Cause? (Person, Situation, please mention)

How did you feel after this

Water ☐ ☐ ☐ ☐ ☐ ☐ ☐ ☐ ☐
☐ ☐ ☐ ☐ ☐ ☐ ☐ ☐ ☐

Vitamins / Supplements Y ☐ N ☐

Eat slow ? Y ☐ N ☐

Stop when full ? Y ☐ N ☐

Exercise Notes

Activity	Minutes	Intensity			Calories Burnt
		Low	Medium	High	
☐ Elliptical					
☐ Walk					
☐ Run / Jog					
☐ Weights					
☐ Swim					
☐ Yoga					
☐ Pilates					
☐ Cycle					
☐ Martial Arts					
☐ Kick Boxing					
☐ Sport					

retching / Warm up Y ☐ N ☐

ainer / Instructor Y ☐ N ☐

"Motivation is what gets you started, Habit is what keeps you going" - Jim Ryon

Comments: (Problem, Injuries, Overall mood, Best/worst moment, Etc...)

minders:

....

....

Met today's goals?

☐☐☐☐

0% 25% 50% 75% 100%

Date:	Week: #	Day: #	Day of week:
		No. of hours sleep (previous night)	

Food Notes

Upon waking

Time:

Breakfast

Time:

Snack 1

Time:

Lunch

Time:

Snack 2

Time:

Snack 3

Time:

Dinner

Time:

Before Sleep

Time:

Water ☐ ☐ ☐ ☐ ☐ ☐ ☐ ☐ ☐
☐ ☐ ☐ ☐ ☐ ☐ ☐ ☐ ☐

Vitamins / Supplements Y ☐ N ☐

Eat slow ? Y ☐ N ☐

Stop when full ? Y ☐ N ☐

Tip

Use beans in your salads. They can only do you good.

Did you eat any "comfort food"?

Y ☐ N ☐

If Yes -
mention the comfort food

What were you feeling at that time?

Cause? (Person, Situation, please mention)

How did you feel after this?

Exercise Notes

Activity	Minutes	Intensity			Calories Burnt
		Low	Medium	High	
☐ Elliptical					
☐ Walk					
☐ Run / Jog					
☐ Weights					
☐ Swim					
☐ Yoga					
☐ Pilates					
☐ Cycle					
☐ Martial Arts					
☐ Kick Boxing					
☐ Sport					

retching / Warm up Y ☐ N ☐

iner / Instructor Y ☐ N ☐

"Celebrate your life"

Comments: (Problem, Injuries, Overall mood, Best/worst moment, Etc...)

minders:

Met today's goals?

0% 25% 50% 75% 100%

Date:	Week: #	Day: #	Day of week:
		No. of hours sleep (previous night)	

Food Notes

Upon waking

Time:

Breakfast

Time:

Snack 1

Time:

Lunch

Time:

Snack 2

Time:

Snack 3

Time:

Dinner

Time:

Before Sleep

Time:

Water ☐ ☐ ☐ ☐ ☐ ☐ ☐ ☐ ☐
☐ ☐ ☐ ☐ ☐ ☐ ☐ ☐ ☐

Vitamins / Supplements Y ☐ N ☐

Eat slow ? Y ☐ N ☐

Stop when full ? Y ☐ N ☐

Tip

Oats: A wonder food - add it to your new lifestyle.

Did you eat any "comfort food"?

Y ☐ N ☐

If Yes -
mention the comfort food

What were you feeling at that time?

Cause? (Person, Situation, please mention)

How did you feel after this?

Exercise Notes

ctivity	Minutes	Intensity			Calories Burnt
		Low	Medium	High	
] Elliptical					
] Walk					
] Run / Jog					
] Weights					
] Swim					
] Yoga					
] Pilates					
] Cycle					
] Martial Arts					
] Kick Boxing					
] Sport					

etching / Warm up Y ☐ N ☐

iner / Instructor Y ☐ N ☐

"We don't stop playing because we grow old;
we grow old because we stop playing" - George Shaw

Comments: (Problem, Injuries, Overall mood, Best/worst moment, Etc...)

ninders:

Met today's goals?

0% 25% 50% 75% 100%

Date: | Week: # | Day: # | Day of week:

No. of hours sleep (previous night)

Food Notes

Upon waking

Time:

Breakfast

Time:

Snack 1

Time:

Lunch

Time:

Snack 2

Time:

Snack 3

Time:

Dinner

Time:

Before Sleep

Time:

Water ☐ ☐ ☐ ☐ ☐ ☐ ☐ ☐ ☐
☐ ☐ ☐ ☐ ☐ ☐ ☐ ☐ ☐

Vitamins / Supplements Y ☐ N ☐

Eat slow ? Y ☐ N ☐

Stop when full ? Y ☐ N ☐

Tip

Make a list of all your favorite foods. You will find that it is possible to incorporate all of them in your food plan.

Did you eat any "comfort food"?

Y ☐ N ☐

If Yes -
mention the comfort food

What were you feeling at that time?

Cause? (Person, Situation, please mention)

How did you feel after this?

Exercise Notes

ctivity	Minutes	Intensity			Calories Burnt
		Low	Medium	High	
] Elliptical					
] Walk					
] Run / Jog					
] Weights					
] Swim					
] Yoga					
] Pilates					
] Cycle					
] Martial Arts					
] Kick Boxing					
] Sport					

etching / Warm up Y ☐ N ☐

iner / Instructor Y ☐ N ☐

"We first make our habits, then our habits make us" - Jhon Dryden

Comments: (Problem, Injuries, Overall mood, Best/worst moment, Etc...)

ninders:

....

....

Met today's goals?

0% 25% 50% 75% 100%

Date: | Week: # | Day: # | Day of week:

No. of hours sleep (previous night)

Food Notes

Upon waking

Time:

Breakfast

Time:

Snack 1

Time:

Lunch

Time:

Snack 2

Time:

Snack 3

Time:

Dinner

Time:

Before Sleep

Time:

Water ☐ ☐ ☐ ☐ ☐ ☐ ☐ ☐ ☐
☐ ☐ ☐ ☐ ☐ ☐ ☐ ☐ ☐

Vitamins / Supplements Y ☐ N ☐

Eat slow ? Y ☐ N ☐

Stop when full ? Y ☐ N ☐

Tip

Instant energy? Snack on nuts, fruits and dry fruits.

Did you eat any "comfort food"?

Y ☐ N ☐

If Yes - mention the comfort food

What were you feeling at that time?

Cause? (Person, Situation, please mention)

How did you feel after this?

Exercise Notes

Activity	Minutes	Intensity			Calories Burnt
		Low	Medium	High	
☐ Elliptical					
☐ Walk					
☐ Run / Jog					
☐ Weights					
☐ Swim					
☐ Yoga					
☐ Pilates					
☐ Cycle					
☐ Martial Arts					
☐ Kick Boxing					
☐ Sport					

retching / Warm up Y ☐ N ☐

ainer / Instructor Y ☐ N ☐

"It's not that some people have will power and others don't; it's that some people are ready to change and others are not." - James Gorden

Comments: (Problem, Injuries, Overall mood, Best/worst moment, Etc...)

minders:

....

....

Met today's goals?

0% 25% 50% 75% 100%

Date: | Week: # | Day: # | Day of week:

No. of hours sleep (previous night)

Food Notes

Upon waking

Time:

Breakfast

Time:

Snack 1

Time:

Lunch

Time:

Snack 2

Time:

Snack 3

Time:

Dinner

Time:

Before Sleep

Time:

Water ☐ ☐ ☐ ☐ ☐ ☐ ☐ ☐ ☐
☐ ☐ ☐ ☐ ☐ ☐ ☐ ☐ ☐

Vitamins / Supplements Y ☐ N ☐

Eat slow ? Y ☐ N ☐

Stop when full ? Y ☐ N ☐

Tip

Are you drinking water through the day? Stay hydrated.

Did you eat any "comfort food"?

Y ☐ N ☐

If Yes -
mention the comfort food

What were you feeling at that time?

Cause? (Person, Situation, please mention)

How did you feel after this?

Exercise Notes

Activity	Minutes	Intensity			Calories Burnt
		Low	Medium	High	
☐ Elliptical					
☐ Walk					
☐ Run / Jog					
☐ Weights					
☐ Swim					
☐ Yoga					
☐ Pilates					
☐ Cycle					
☐ Martial Arts					
☐ Kick Boxing					
☐ Sport					

etching / Warm up Y ☐ N ☐

iner / Instructor Y ☐ N ☐

"You don't have to see the whole staircase - Just take the first step"
- Martin Luther King

Comments: (Problem, Injuries, Overall mood, Best/worst moment, Etc...)

ninders:

Met today's goals?

0% 25% 50% 75% 100%

Date:	Week: #	Day: #	Day of week:
		No. of hours sleep (previous night)	

Food Notes

Upon waking

Time:

Breakfast

Time:

Snack 1

Time:

Lunch

Time:

Snack 2

Time:

Snack 3

Time:

Dinner

Time:

Before Sleep

Time:

Water ☐ ☐ ☐ ☐ ☐ ☐ ☐ ☐ ☐
☐ ☐ ☐ ☐ ☐ ☐ ☐ ☐ ☐

Vitamins / Supplements Y ☐ N ☐

Eat slow ? Y ☐ N ☐

Stop when full ? Y ☐ N ☐

Tip

Emotional hunger is sudden and urgent. Physical hunger is gradual.

Did you eat any "comfort food"?

Y ☐ N ☐

If Yes -
mention the comfort food

What were you feeling at that time?

Cause? (Person, Situation, please mention)

How did you feel after this?

Exercise Notes

ctivity	Minutes	Intensity			Calories Burnt
		Low	Medium	High	
] Elliptical					
] Walk					
] Run / Jog					
] Weights					
] Swim					
] Yoga					
] Pilates					
] Cycle					
] Martial Arts					
] Kick Boxing					
] Sport					

etching / Warm up Y ☐ N ☐

iner / Instructor Y ☐ N ☐

'Sometime it's the smallest decision that can change your life forever" - Kerry Russel

Comments: (Problem, Injuries, Overall mood, Best/worst moment, Etc...)

ninders:

Met today's goals?

0% 25% 50% 75% 100%

Your Scribble Space

(Take your favorite color pen, crayon, pencil and scribble happy thoughts, words, and feelings below, or just paste a picture of someone you love and care about. This is your space, make it happy, vibrant and colorful.)

Last week's happiest moment ______________________

Not so good moment ______________________

Something nice that someone said to you ______________________

Something nice that you said to or did for someone ______________________

Something special you want to do for someone next week ______________________

Are you happy and motivated to stay healthy and fit ? (if not mention why) ______________________

A reward you want to give yourself for staying on track with your fitness goals ______________________

Weekly Goals ____________ ____________

Plan Your Week

	Mon	Tue	Wed	Thur	Fri	Sat	Sun
xercise							
wim							
Valk							
un							
lliptical							
ycle							
Veights							
ports							
oga							
ther:							
est day							
ood							
at outs							
rder in							
etox							
eligious fast							
leep							
Hours							
Hours							
7 Hours							
lassage							

These are your goals for the week. Strive to achieve them.
"A goal without an action plan, is a dream"

Date: | Week: # | Day: # | Day of week:

No. of hours sleep (previous night)

Food Notes

Upon waking

Time:

Breakfast

Time:

Snack 1

Time:

Lunch

Time:

Snack 2

Time:

Snack 3

Time:

Dinner

Time:

Before Sleep

Time:

Water ☐ ☐ ☐ ☐ ☐ ☐ ☐ ☐ ☐
☐ ☐ ☐ ☐ ☐ ☐ ☐ ☐ ☐

Vitamins / Supplements Y ☐ N ☐

Eat slow ? Y ☐ N ☐

Stop when full ? Y ☐ N ☐

Tip

Do regular health checkups. Prevention is better than cure.

Did you eat any "comfort food"?

Y ☐ N ☐

If Yes -
mention the comfort food

What were you feeling at that time?

Cause? (Person, Situation, please mention)

How did you feel after this

Exercise Notes

Activity	Minutes	Intensity			Calories Burnt
		Low	Medium	High	
☐ Elliptical					
☐ Walk					
☐ Run / Jog					
☐ Weights					
☐ Swim					
☐ Yoga					
☐ Pilates					
☐ Cycle					
☐ Martial Arts					
☐ Kick Boxing					
☐ Sport					

retching / Warm up Y ☐ N ☐

ainer / Instructor Y ☐ N ☐

"Leave your comfort zone; Engage in challenge"

Comments: (Problem, Injuries, Overall mood, Best/worst moment, Etc...)

minders:

....

....

Met today's goals?

0% 25% 50% 75% 100%

Date: | Week: # | Day: # | Day of week:

No. of hours sleep (previous night)

Food Notes

Upon waking

Time:

Breakfast

Time:

Snack 1

Time:

Lunch

Time:

Snack 2

Time:

Snack 3

Time:

Dinner

Time:

Before Sleep

Time:

Tip

Limit acidic foods like tea and coffee. They are inflammatory and too much leads to joint pain and aches.

Did you eat any "comfort food"?

Y ☐ N ☐

If Yes - mention the comfort food

What were you feeling at that time?

Cause? (Person, Situation, please mention)

How did you feel after this?

Water ☐ ☐ ☐ ☐ ☐ ☐ ☐ ☐ ☐
☐ ☐ ☐ ☐ ☐ ☐ ☐ ☐ ☐

Vitamins / Supplements Y ☐ N ☐

Eat slow ? Y ☐ N ☐

Stop when full ? Y ☐ N ☐

Exercise Notes

Activity	Minutes	Intensity			Calories Burnt
		Low	Medium	High	
☐ Elliptical					
☐ Walk					
☐ Run / Jog					
☐ Weights					
☐ Swim					
☐ Yoga					
☐ Pilates					
☐ Cycle					
☐ Martial Arts					
☐ Kick Boxing					
☐ Sport					

etching / Warm up Y ☐ N ☐

iner / Instructor Y ☐ N ☐

"It's not that you can't. It's what you haven't. Reprogram Your thinking."

Comments: (Problem, Injuries, Overall mood, Best/worst moment, Etc...)

minders:

Met today's goals?

0% 25% 50% 75% 100%

Date: | Week: # | Day: # | Day of week:

No. of hours sleep (previous night)

Food Notes

Upon waking

Time:

Breakfast

Time:

Snack 1

Time:

Lunch

Time:

Snack 2

Time:

Snack 3

Time:

Dinner

Time:

Before Sleep

Time:

Water ☐ ☐ ☐ ☐ ☐ ☐ ☐ ☐ ☐
☐ ☐ ☐ ☐ ☐ ☐ ☐ ☐ ☐

Vitamins / Supplements Y ☐ N ☐

Eat slow ? Y ☐ N ☐

Stop when full ? Y ☐ N ☐

Tip

Smoking and alcohol are the unhealthiest combination.

Did you eat any "comfort food"?

Y ☐ N ☐

If Yes -
mention the comfort food

What were you feeling at that time?

Cause? (Person, Situation, please mention)

How did you feel after this?

Exercise Notes

ctivity	Minutes	Intensity			Calories Burnt
		Low	Medium	High	
☐ Elliptical					
☐ Walk					
☐ Run / Jog					
☐ Weights					
☐ Swim					
☐ Yoga					
☐ Pilates					
☐ Cycle					
☐ Martial Arts					
☐ Kick Boxing					
☐ Sport					

etching / Warm up Y ☐ N ☐

iner / Instructor Y ☐ N ☐

"Be silent. Completely silent; and observe your relationship with yourself."

Comments: (Problem, Injuries, Overall mood, Best/worst moment, Etc...)

minders:

Met today's goals?

0% 25% 50% 75% 100%

Date:	Week: #	Day: #	Day of week:
		No. of hours sleep (previous night)	

Food Notes

Upon waking

Time:

Breakfast

Time:

Snack 1

Time:

Lunch

Time:

Snack 2

Time:

Snack 3

Time:

Dinner

Time:

Before Sleep

Time:

Water ☐ ☐ ☐ ☐ ☐ ☐ ☐ ☐ ☐
☐ ☐ ☐ ☐ ☐ ☐ ☐ ☐ ☐

Vitamins / Supplements Y ☐ N ☐

Eat slow ? Y ☐ N ☐

Stop when full ? Y ☐ N ☐

Tip

Any sprouted food is super rich in nutrients. Add them to your soups, salads or main - course. Wash them well.

Did you eat any "comfort food"?

Y ☐ N ☐

If Yes -
mention the comfort food

What were you feeling at that time?

Cause? (Person, Situation, please mention)

How did you feel after this?

Exercise Notes

ctivity	Minutes	Intensity			Calories Burnt
		Low	Medium	High	
] Elliptical					
] Walk					
] Run / Jog					
] Weights					
] Swim					
] Yoga					
] Pilates					
] Cycle					
] Martial Arts					
] Kick Boxing					
] Sport					

etching / Warm up Y ☐ N ☐

iner / Instructor Y ☐ N ☐

"The only thing that you have complete control over, is your own mental attitude."

Comments: (Problem, Injuries, Overall mood, Best/worst moment, Etc...)

ninders:

....

....

Met today's goals?

0% 25% 50% 75% 100%

Date: | Week: # | Day: # | Day of week:

No. of hours sleep (previous night)

Food Notes

Upon waking

Time:

Breakfast

Time:

Snack 1

Time:

Lunch

Time:

Snack 2

Time:

Snack 3

Time:

Dinner

Time:

Before Sleep

Time:

Water ☐ ☐ ☐ ☐ ☐ ☐ ☐ ☐ ☐
☐ ☐ ☐ ☐ ☐ ☐ ☐ ☐ ☐

Vitamins / Supplements Y ☐ N ☐

Eat slow ? Y ☐ N ☐

Stop when full ? Y ☐ N ☐

Tip

Home cooked food is the healthiest option.

Did you eat any "comfort food"?

Y ☐ N ☐

If Yes - mention the comfort food

What were you feeling at that time?

Cause? (Person, Situation, please mention)

How did you feel after this?

Exercise Notes

Activity	Minutes	Intensity			Calories Burnt
		Low	Medium	High	
☐ Elliptical					
☐ Walk					
☐ Run / Jog					
☐ Weights					
☐ Swim					
☐ Yoga					
☐ Pilates					
☐ Cycle					
☐ Martial Arts					
☐ Kick Boxing					
☐ Sport					

retching / Warm up Y ☐ N ☐

ainer / Instructor Y ☐ N ☐

"Does your fitness goal excite your imagination."

Comments: (Problem, Injuries, Overall mood, Best/worst moment, Etc...)

eminders:

Met today's goals?

0% 25% 50% 75% 100%

Date: | Week: # | Day: # | Day of week:

No. of hours sleep (previous night)

Food Notes

Upon waking

Time:

Breakfast

Time:

Snack 1

Time:

Lunch

Time:

Snack 2

Time:

Snack 3

Time:

Dinner

Time:

Before Sleep

Time:

Water ☐ ☐ ☐ ☐ ☐ ☐ ☐ ☐ ☐
☐ ☐ ☐ ☐ ☐ ☐ ☐ ☐ ☐

Vitamins / Supplements Y ☐ N ☐

Eat slow ? Y ☐ N ☐

Stop when full ? Y ☐ N ☐

Tip

Choose a-la-carte over buffet. Its proven that you will always eat more at a buffet.

Did you eat any "comfort food"?

Y ☐ N ☐

If Yes -
mention the comfort food

What were you feeling at that time?

Cause? (Person, Situation, please mention)

How did you feel after this?

Exercise Notes

Activity	Minutes	Intensity			Calories Burnt
		Low	Medium	High	
☐ Elliptical					
☐ Walk					
☐ Run / Jog					
☐ Weights					
☐ Swim					
☐ Yoga					
☐ Pilates					
☐ Cycle					
☐ Martial Arts					
☐ Kick Boxing					
☐ Sport					

etching / Warm up Y ☐ N ☐

iner / Instructor Y ☐ N ☐

"There are two kinds of light - The glow what illuminates and the glare that obscures" - James Thurber

Comments: (Problem, Injuries, Overall mood, Best/worst moment, Etc...)

ninders:

Met today's goals?

0% 25% 50% 75% 100%

Date: | Week: # | Day: # | Day of week:

No. of hours sleep (previous night)

Food Notes

Upon waking

Time:

Breakfast

Time:

Snack 1

Time:

Lunch

Time:

Snack 2

Time:

Snack 3

Time:

Dinner

Time:

Before Sleep

Time:

Water ☐ ☐ ☐ ☐ ☐ ☐ ☐ ☐ ☐
☐ ☐ ☐ ☐ ☐ ☐ ☐ ☐ ☐

Vitamins / Supplements Y ☐ N ☐

Eat slow ? Y ☐ N ☐

Stop when full ? Y ☐ N ☐

Tip

Fiber rich foods will improve your health and weight.

Did you eat any "comfort food"?

Y ☐ N ☐

If Yes - mention the comfort food

What were you feeling at that time?

Cause? (Person, Situation, please mention)

How did you feel after this?

Exercise Notes

ctivity	Minutes	Intensity			Calories Burnt
		Low	Medium	High	
] Elliptical					
] Walk					
] Run / Jog					
] Weights					
] Swim					
] Yoga					
] Pilates					
] Cycle					
] Martial Arts					
] Kick Boxing					
] Sport					

etching / Warm up Y ☐ N ☐

ner / Instructor Y ☐ N ☐

"The most important choice you make is what you choose to make important."

Comments: (Problem, Injuries, Overall mood, Best/worst moment, Etc...)

ninders:

Met today's goals?

0% 25% 50% 75% 100%

Your Scribble Space

(Take your favorite color pen, crayon, pencil and scribble happy thoughts, words, and feelings below, or just paste a picture of someone you love and care about. This is your space, make it happy, vibrant and colorful.)

Last week's happiest moment ____________________

Not so good moment ____________________

Something nice that someone said to you ____________________

Something nice that you said to or did for someone ____________________

Something special you want to do for someone next week ____________________

Are you happy and motivated to stay healthy and fit ? (if not mention why) ____________________

A reward you want to give yourself for staying on track with your fitness goals ____________________

Weekly Progress

WEEKLY PROGRESS

	Week 1	Week 2	Week 3
Weights			
Body fat %			
Blood pressure			
Resting heart rate			
Total no.of exercise days			
Average hours of sleep per night			

	Week 4	Week 5	Week 6
Weights			
Body fat %			
Blood pressure			
Resting heart rate			
Total no.of exercise days			
Average hours of sleep per night			

	Week 7	Week 8
Weights		
Body fat %		
Blood pressure		
Resting heart rate		
Total no.of exercise days		
Average hours of sleep per night		

CONGRATULATIONS

On completing your 8-week journey of 'food journaling'. I am sure you would have either lost weight or taken your fitness levels to a new height.

If not, go through the journal and compare entries week on week. It will tell you a story of what went well and what did not. And don't feel sad or de-motivated. At the most, you would have learnt what obstacles are keeping you from achieving your goal, and as you flip through the pages, you will determine what you need to do. You may find it necessary to re-shape your goal or make a larger goal, but your valuable entries will make you realize a lot about your lifestyle and the things you need to do. It's never too late.

If this worked for you, you will realize how simple it is to get fit.

Read frequently through the text in this book and educate yourself to become your own nutritionist and fitness consultant.

Shape your goal, believe in it, eat, sleep and drink it, and it's no miracle that you will achieve it. Keep it simple.

"I ridiculed the idea of such a concept ever working. But Luke gently encouraged me to try it for 3 days, which I did, and then it became 6 days and then a week and then 3 months. I lost 6.5 kilos and inches off my thighs and waist, just by writing in entries everyday, and making simple lifestyle changes. It's a powerful tool and I began to look forward to writing in my journal every night before bed"

Caroline Ruth, Vancouver.

"I would never work out before I began using this journal. The very fact of me having to take responsibility to write whether I exercised or not at the end of the day, slowly got me to begin with a regime. And as the weeks flew by and I saw a tick in the "yes" box for exercise, my motivation levels grew and now it's a new lifestyle. I can't go a day without doing some amount of physical activity"

Ajay Mehta, New Jersey.

"It didn't work for me, but I have to tell you that when I flipped through all my pages, I found that I had filled them randomly, and I noticed a pattern of comfort foods that I would just not reduce or give up. It then struck me that this concept can work only if I have a goal set and make daily entries into the journal, So I'm starting this exercise all over again with my goal shaped to lose 18 pounds"

Name withheld as per clients request.

In Gratitude

My sincere thanks and gratitude to ~

My Family: For always being there. Thank you for all your support and unconditional love.

Nitin Dang: You inspired me to think beyond. Thank you.

Nirav Modi: The first 45 minutes I spent with you at your office were miserable. You made me feel like I had it all messed up. You hurled questions at me like missiles, but you made me introspect and "shape my goal". That inspired change in me. Thank you for being my mentor.

Neena Sheth: You encouraged me to get this far and to strike a balance in all that I do. Several pieces of this book and several ideas were born by the lake, at Lake Isle, New York. Thank you for your generosity, hospitality and for being the way you are.

Natashya Phillips: Thank you for all your support, encouragement and patience.

All my friends: I know I missed several outings and fun trips with you. Thank you for your understanding. Now you know what I was busy with. Thank you.

Willard Kitchen: You created 'space and opportunity' for me to roll with this. Thank you.

Amay Sheth: Your dedication and success in reaching your goal inspired me deeply to get started with this.

Samantha Murton: You have been an inspiration through the journey. Thank you for all your words of wisdom, your patience and moreover your valuable time.

Liwayway Langit: Thank you for your continuous support and encouragement.

Ami Modi: Your constant follow-up kept me working on this. Your discipline and integrity inspires me. Thank you.

Arthur Ward: That cosmic connect still exists! Thank you.

Maulik Doshi: You were on my back from day one. Appreciate your support, ideas and motivation. Thank you.

Gouri and Mohit Gupta: Sharing your thoughts and scraps inspired me to 'add energy' to this book. Thank you.

My Team at work (IBM, Mumbai): Philipose John, Nitin Dang, Ravindra Bhatia. You guys are the best. Thank you for your support and patience.

Pritan Sone (Manager, Barista's): Thank you for your hospitality and patience. It's been a pleasure writing out of your outlet.

Chetan and Smita Choksi: Thank you for all the wisdom shared, and for the use of your comfortable library in Antwerp.

Ajay and Nandini Mehta: Your family values and integrity inspires me. I'm happy I know you.

Amar Jadhav: It's rare to come across designers who are so patient, innovative and understanding. Thank you for all your support and guidance to make this a success. Please pass my gratitude on to your team.

Deanne Travasso: Coaching is never a one way process. When you evolve as a result of coaching, and your own effort and dedication, it is the best inspiration.

My family at Curlies, Goa: Thank you for your hospitality. I have the fondest memories thinking and writing out of Curlies.

All my clients and friends across the globe: Every counseling or training session educates and motivates me to hold on to my passion of helping and encouraging people to get fit and live happy lives. Each of you inspire me in different ways. Thank you.

The Forces of Nature: I have learnt not to argue, fight or resist you. I will flow with you and live in peace. Thank you.